A Tinker's Secret

Robert G. McPhee

YouCaxton Publications
24 High Street, Bishop's Castle, Shropshire. SY3 8JX
www.youCaxton.co.uk
Published in Great Britain by
Robert MacPhee
Copyright © Robert MacPhee 2006
The Author asserts the moral right to
be identified as the author of this work.
ISBN 978-1-909644-01-4
Cover Illustration © 2006 Fritha Scowcroft, Frith Art

Set in Adobe Garamond Pro.
Printed and bound in Great Britain.

Robert McPhee

Acknowledgements

For Dusty Miller, my late friend and mentor, who taught me through the years, to open my mind and see what lay dormant.

With sincere thanks, to the following for the encouragement without which this book may never have left my beloved cellar: to Geordie and Ellen, just for being my mum and dad, to my sister Tricia whose information and memory were invaluable to me, to Ali my editor, for the encouragement, the red pen and kind works, to Fritha for the recreation of my Grandfather's wagon in the cover illustration, to Alan for turning my scribbling into a professional-looking article, of which I am very proud, and to friends Sally and Clive who waded through the early editions and gave honest and constructive criticism.

But most of all, to Maureen my rock, who had the belief that forced me to see it through.

§

A secret held and best untold,
The weight of burden he canny unfold.
At last life's tangled trick's revealed,
Too late, the tinker boy is gone.

Chapter One

Baptism Of Fire

A soft breeze ruffled their hair as they meandered their way toward Wick, but now blue skies turned to grey and the breeze suddenly stiffened. Highland weather is unpredictable and can be prone to sudden change. Dada looked west into the breeze and furrowed his brow in concern but this was more because my birth was imminent than from any concern for the weather. At any other time, he would have looked for a tree for shelter and to sit out a storm, but now my mother's condition must force them to run before it. 'A baptism of fire ye had, Geordie,' he always said when relating this story.

Tinker history came down to me by way of stories like these, told each night at bedtime and added to by visiting story tellers and others who had something to add to the colourful canvas my Dada painted of our traveling days in the wild. The stories told that my Dada, as a young man, bore a great resemblance to both his father and grandfather before him, all had the black curly hair and swarthy good looks that could mistake them for Mediterranean men rather than highland Scots, and all were blessed with the strength of stallions.

My Dada, they said, had fallen in love with his fifteen-year-old cousin Sarah, a tall, beautiful girl with the spirit to go with her red hair and the startling blue eyes of an angel and it was she who would become my mother. Dada had spent time learning the tin-smith's skills from his father-in-law but rewarded him by making off with his only daughter and, though ungracious, his marriage, tinker-style, to a first cousin was not an unusual occurrence. My grandfather's gift to Dada of a wagon and pony was his only comment on the match, and they left with his blessing.

Dada and Mother travelled between villages selling the pots he made and doing odd jobs at harvest time. That was their life, peaceful and tranquil with trout to tickle and game to snare. Their moors provided a bountiful and free lifestyle. They wandered the heather-clad hills, making love under the warm summer sun, heading for home whenever the wretched weather closed in. Jonno, my brother, was born from the wagon with Dada's help and they continued their travellers' life unimpeded. On the first day of every month, they would join the gathering tinkers in Wick, where Mother would gut the herring catch alongside all the other young tinker women while Dada refurbished their wagon and stocked up with necessities for mother and baby.

All was well until my mother fell pregnant again and was caught out in the wild. They'd had no reason to be concerned but this time the baby was a breach and without help the infant died. This was their first real disaster and one that would live with my mother all her days. The little baby was laid by the loch, and my mother's prayers and tears were buried with him. Dada and Mother swore it would never happen again and that they would always have help on hand should they need it.

Through the stories, I learned of my own birth at the Latheron Workhouse, and of my parents' perilous trip by wagon through a blizzard, in an attempt to reach the safety of the family, gathered and waiting at the harbour in Wick. Dada painted a vivid picture of this blizzard that caught him unawares and unprepared, himself, my mother and little Jonno, now four years old. My mother was in the last stages of pregnancy and I was desperate to be born and this was why she agreed to my birth at the Latheron Workhouse - but only as a desperate last resort.

The Workhouse was situated midway between where Mother's labour pains began and where the family was in Wick, and it was their only hope of help. Its rules, Dada said, would only allow the birth and one day's free respite then we'd have to move on or work our keep. The place was taboo to Mother, the stories about it, that she'd grown up with, told of people swallowed up inside and never able to work their freedom. Dada had left her there but promised, before leaving, that he'd be waiting outside the doors at dawn. He planned to pitch our tent by the loch-side down below and to allow mother and baby to gain strength there before moving on.

On February 22nd, the coldest day of the winter so far that year, I drew my first breath and my breathe signalled the start of a snow storm of such ferocity that it battered Dada and little Jonno to a standstill. Jonno told of the cold he felt in his fingers while scraping the ice from the sticks and how his tears froze on his cheeks in the raw wind. It was necessary, Dada said, to find shelter and warmth before dealing with hunger and sleep and, tears or not, the job must be done. Jonno said he was sent time and again to gather more sticks, while Dada struggled to pitch the tent.

The tent up and the sticks laid, Dada wanted paper from the chest in the wagon. 'Paper, Jonno,' Dada said softly and Jonno scurried to the cart and lifted the heavy lid off the chest where they kept the newspapers. Dada was always careful to keep the chest well stocked, collecting discarded papers whenever they passed through a town and, although they couldn't read or write, they'd look at the pictures and make up their own stories. It was a favourite game for winter evenings around the fire. Jonno told how he'd picked up what turned out to be a Wick Journal, dated 4th February 1915. It had been just over two weeks old, he'd handed the middle pages to Dada.

'Who's this man, Dada and why's he looking at me?' Jonno had asked, pointing his frozen finger at the front-page picture. 'Wherever I move,' he said, 'his eyes still see me.'

Dada shook his head impatiently. 'At this moment in time, boy, it's of no importance.' He held out his hand, Jonno was reluctant to give up his picture but Dada insisted. Jonno handed the page over and watched as the face was shredded yet still he saw the remaining eye looking at him.

'A match then, boy,' Dada said, 'they'll be in the chest there, be quick.'

He'd taught Jonno to be careful not to waste more than one match, they were a lifeline, a precious commodity, he arranged the kindling carefully before scraping the match-head on his boot. Watching the kindling catch and the flame grow, Dada placed selected sticks, pointing skywards, in a pyramid around the base, they would funnel the smoke toward the roof of the tent to escape through the small opening above. Jonno watched the picture curl and blacken before finally bursting into flame and, even as it burned, the eye still seemed to look straight at him. The picture emblazoned on the front page was of Kitchener, (although Dada didn't know it at the time), captioned in bold letters by the slogan 'Your Country Needs You.' The headline urged all young men to go to marshalling points and answer the call to arms, for King and Country.

'If I could've read it, boy, I would've been moved to laughter,' Dada told me later. The dispossessed highlanders, who had been scattered to the four winds and forgotten, were now finally being recognised, and wanted even, to fight and die for 'King and Country,' but the reporter making a case for the justification of the war was wasting his time in Dada's company. All the written arguments were lost on him and he remained, for now, in blissful ignorance, unaware of the mass exodus to the recruitment centres all over the British Isles.

The fire was blazing now and it was time to cook and look after the living.

'Come Jonno,' Dada said, 'we've some fishing to do.'

Jonno admitted to me that he'd never felt colder than when they had left the tent and set off hand in hand in the snow to where a brook ran into the loch.

'Watch and learn, boy,' Dada said, but all Jonno could do was shiver.

'The art of patience is the key, Jonno,' Dada continued. 'You trace the brook back to a large pool below a fall, lay your hand in the icy water by the edge of the bank and keep it very still.'

Jonno lay by Dada's side, his teeth chattering fit to crack, and waited patiently for Dada to tempt a fish from under the bank. He watched, cold but fascinated, as the trout, mesmerised by Dada's finger stroking its throat, swam into his hand and, with a flick of Dada's now frozen fingers, it was caught. Hunger hurried them back to camp and Jonno watched as the trout was made ready for the pot.

'Now,' Dada said. 'Fetch the skillet, boy, and hang it from a tripod over the fire. Fill it with snow and give me ten minutes to prepare a feast.'

Jonno was still shivering as he sat close to Dada with his hands stretched out to the fire and his fingers stinging with the pain. Meanwhile Dada gave a running commentary on the cooking of Tinker stew.

'You slice a carrot so and follow it with an onion into the pot of boiling water, then stir, Jonno. It turns cloudy, boy, by the juice of the fish. Then add a handful of barley and wait a while. When it swells, it's ready. If you eat it too early, the barley will swell in your stomach and give you a terrible pain.' Dada looked down to see him gently snoring and rousted him up. 'Jonno, go fetch the plates,' he'd said, 'and never sleep hungry, or the next time ye wake it may be to face yer maker.

The meal was all the nicer for the waiting and it was steaming hot. It seemed to set their stomachs on fire. Jonno found out later that the fire in their stomachs was due more to the habit of slipping a glass of whisky into the pot without anyone being any the wiser. Dada's father had taught him the habit and it had served him well enough during the cold winters. It was time now to gather some fuel, bank up the fire and see to Jen, the pony.

'First things, always first, Jonno,' Dada said. Jen would be their life-line out of there and it was best to let her go free, so she could find a place out of the snow.

Jonno later told how he loved these times with Dada, lying warm from the whisky and hot food, snuggled next to the fire, under a sheepskin cured by my mother. 'Dada would tell me stories of his childhood,' Jonno remembered, 'on Orkney and about the history of the family, as it had been passed on to him.' Jonno was asleep now and gently snoring, warm, with a full stomach and tipsy from the whisky, but Dada wasn't ready to sleep yet, his senses were alert, the storm was howling and the tent sagged with the weight of the snow. An alarm bell was ringing in his head as he stared into the fire, trying to make sense of a feeling that something was stirring.

Tomorrow he would collect Sarah and the baby and they'd spend a few days there for her to rest and recover and then move on. The journey up the hillside to the workhouse was a painstaking battle. They inched their way forward, Jonno clutching old Jen's tail and with his face pressed against her hindquarters, his boots filled with snow, his feet so cold he was hardly able to feel them. 'That, Geordie, was definitely my worst memory,' he told me later.

Mother said she'd dreaded being left alone at the workhouse and prayed the whole time for her salvation. When I made my entrance screaming defiantly, she said she blessed me for the spirit that had given her the strength and heart to face what was to come. When it was over, we were led to the door to face the freezing blizzard, Mother clutching me to her breast, tightly wrapped in her shawl, and the door slammed shut behind us.

Dada appeared out of the mist with Jonno snivelling at his side to say that we had to move on to Wick immediately or risk being snowed in. This bad news mother took without a word of complaint, though she said later that it had filled her with fear for my survival - and Dada's description of that trip made me feel glad I had no memory of it. Poor Jonno suffered with frozen toes and fingers with only the whisky to warm him.

All Dada said was that survival was what counted and that hardship would put iron in our blood. Jonno often told me of the things he'd learned with Dada in those early years and how he was proud that Dada had said that they were a team. He was truly a tinker boy though barely knee-high to a grasshopper. For me, Mother had other plans, she'd made a promise to God when lying in that workhouse bed - that I would be the one to break the travelling mould and learn the school things of which she and Dada had little knowledge, and, if I were to fulfil her dream, we would have to change, we would have to settle and stay in Wick.

The story of our struggle from the workhouse spread quickly around Wick, and those who heard the details unanimously agreed that it was a miracle that we'd all come out alive. The harbour front was solid with wagons when we arrived and the young women were furiously gutting the herring in the driving snow, but we'd arrived late and, although there were plenty of boats, all full of herring, Mother's place at the table had been lost, and that was to be a sad loss for all of us. While mother displayed me to the female members of the family, Dada was shooed off to a meeting at the cave on the hill. This was unusual news, Dada had said. He knew well that the men would normally be half drunk at the Highlander pub by now and the first rounds of the arm wrestling contest would be under way. There had to be something serious in the air for the men to be meeting without a drink.

§

Chapter Two

A War To End Wars

Dada climbed the hillside to the cave that served as a meeting place in times of decision-making and, as he arrived, he heard Tam Mackay highlighting the news of a 'war to end all wars' to the bemused crowd of men. Tam was able to read thanks to his grammar school education, and he could analyse the political situation and what it might mean. He was no longer a travelling man, and he tried from time to time to persuade travelling tinker families to settle for the sake of their children. Now he was warning them about what he thought might happen if they allowed themselves to get carried away in the heat of the moment. They were simple people, he knew well enough, and easily led - and if one decided to join up, they might all follow suit. But Tam didn't talk their language anymore, he was neither tinker nor townie, accepted by both but listened to by neither. He finished with a warning, Dada said: 'it'll be a nasty business but mark me - it's none of ours.'

Dada was stunned by Tam's news, he scanned the silent crowd to gauge their mood. They were all looking for a lead and it was Dada's brother William, who rose from the crowd, pushing and throwing men out of his way as he crashed on to the hastily erected stage of empty herring crates covered by board, which shuddered under his weight. Uncle William held sway among the tinker men and he spoke the kind of language they all understood. He was as wide as he was tall with the black hair of his mother and the barrel chest of my grandfather Isaac. He believed anything could be settled with his huge fists and he'd proved the point on numerous occasions, according to whoever was telling the story.

'Yer Uncle Will,' Tam told me years later, 'strutted around the stage waving his fist like a club, drawing a huge roar. What I would have done, Geordie, for a response, like that,' Tam sighed.

Will's message boomed out and though crude they were words they understood.

'We're ganging no fucking where and if those saft English bastards think we'll spill one drop of tinker blood to save their miserable skins, they can kiss my arse,' he'd said, baring his huge behind to the crowd who whistled and roared their approval of his solution, Tam included.

An anonymous voice from the crowd wanted to know what would happen if the authorities served them with the papers.

'If they serve us with the papers, then we'll ram their fucking papers so far up their arses, by the time they find them, we'll all be bloody lang gane,' roared Uncle Will.

'But what if they send the army after us?'

'They send the soldier boys after me and I'll set my Elizabeth on 'em.'

Tam smiled at his recollection. 'Your aunt Elizabeth was an awesome woman and Will was immensely proud of her. At the tender age of eighteen she'd become a legend in tinker circles. She was a tall, solid girl, big-boned and with a healthy covering of meat, as Will lovingly described her, and she could fight as good as any of them but twice as dirty. The cast-iron ladle she carried hanging from her waist, had been made for her by your Dada, as a wedding present, along with a tureen for the purpose of ladling soup, but in her hands it became a fearsome weapon. The very thought of being tracked by your aunt Elizabeth,' Tam said, 'drew a sigh from the crowd. Will offered a prayer for her unknown victims and crossed himself, and the crowd had murmured amen, followed by a huge cheer.'

Tales tell that Elizabeth not only fought like a man but entered the arm-wrestling competitions alongside Dada, often winning by dubious means though no one ever thought it prudent to complain. Her favourite ploy was to rest her huge breasts on the table under the nose of her competitors, mesmerising them as she rolled them from side to side with the movement of her arm.

'It's like tickling trout,' Will once told Tam, 'a beautiful sight to see.'

'The competitors,' Tam giggled, 'would lose momentary concentration and she'd smash their resistance down to the table and pick up her winnings. Actually, although she boasted a man's strength, she had a pretty face and harboured a woman's heart, she could be as gentle and as sensitive as any, though few adversaries would testify to it.'

Will's speech made Tam's point rather better than he could have made it himself, and the plan of non-co-operation was agreed by all. As soon as the women were paid, Tam said, they'd be off into the desolate moorland to await news of defeat or victory, they didn't much care which. This was tough for Dada what with me being so young. Dada told us it was the most difficult decision he had ever had to make.

'You being just a new born Geordie, and your mother needing some rest, were the most important things. My decision to stay didn't sit well with your mother but I'd not leave until she'd made a full recovery and now that we'd missed the herring catch, we'd have to wait on the next boat to try to get some work unloading and sell a few pots. She pleaded with me for us to take you back out into the wilderness and lay low until it was all over, and Will backed her up and argued that we should all leave together and even Tam added his opinion, to persuade Dada to leave.

'It'll be like old times,' Will had said, 'we'll have a few jars and break a few heads on the way. What do you say boy?'

'I was sorely tempted, Geordie,' said Dada, 'for all his bawdy ways, Will was family. But my mind was made up. I'd stay and take my chances. Right or wrong, I stayed, against all their best efforts to snatch me away.'

'Your pride, Rabbie boy,' Will said as a parting comment, will be your downfall,' but he wished him luck and left shaking his head at Mother.

Dada had little time for the English, but he'd only leave Wick if he wasn't challenged, so if they served him the papers, then he'd sign-up.

That night the army moved into town, led by a brass band. The soldiers were armed with papers more deadly than bullets and full of reassuring tales of British successes and an imminent victory. The locals flocked in droves to sign up for what was said to be just a mopping-up operation. In reality they would be pitched into bloody trench-fighting and most of a whole generation would never return.

Mother pleaded again with Dada, to take us under cover of darkness back out into the wild, but Dada still refused. He faced a dilemma, a direct challenge to his manhood, so mother said: he wouldn't turn tail and run, although there wouldn't be a tinker in a hundred miles who'd blame him if he did.

'That wasn't your Dada's way,' Tam said, 'not that Will and the others were cowards, Geordie, far from it. Will would call it self-preservation, everything in Will's world was etched in black and white: stay or go, live or die. For him it was a simple choice but for your Dada it was different, he had to stand and be counted. Some might call it stupid pride and your mother called it desertion.'

Next day Dada was served his papers and the argument was settled, he was enlisted into the Argyle and Southern Highlanders, an infantry regiment, which encompassed a squad of men, all under five foot five, whose job would be to sneak over into no-mans-land before the main advance. He was one of the five-footers whose size would set them apart. 'The Ladies from Hell' was the name they earned, because of their kilts. They were feared by the enemy because they drifted over the trenches like phantoms in the pitch darkness, giving no quarter.

'This then was our destiny, Geordie, to kill or be killed.'

The Argyle and Southern Highlanders were shipped out within the week with no time for proper training. They were issued with rifles and uniforms: Khaki jackets, kilts, woollen socks and boots. The commanding officer told Dada that he wouldn't presume to teach a tinker anything about the art of cunning or stealth and added that Dada would need every scrap of it and more - if he were ever to see his beloved mountains again. The officer made it very clear that a tinker in uniform couldn't be considered to be a proper soldier, but he wished Dada well just the same.

We all went to have a family photograph taken and that photo would be all that Mother had to cling to in the lonely nights to come, that and a lock of his curly hair that she stole that night. She said she'd talk to him, holding the curl, of the days cleaning, of the naughtiness of the children and how similar Geordie was to him. She willed her love to him, to give him strength, and prayed that the iron in his veins would keep his tender side hidden and not cause him to make any fatal errors.

'The warnings and the rumours of the demoralising hell that awaited us, Geordie, were handed down by the seamen on the ship over, they'd taken the wounded and dying off the beaches. We were staggered to hear of the mass slaughter of soldiers at the front but the news only served to stiffen my determination to survive. Not for me, to die like a rat in a trench, I'd be careful and patient, boy, nor would I succumb (as the soldiers in the stories we'd been told had) to reckless charges at the enemy trenches, their will broken and acting rashly out of temporary insanity. I had ye all to come back to and you needed me all in one piece.'

With the shores of France looming on the horizon, Dada said he made a promise to us that he'd be back, but until then he'd banish all thoughts of us from his mind and concentrate all his instincts on the battles ahead and, if he had to be hard and callous to survive then, God forgive him, he would be.

Mother said she wept after Dada had gone, clutching the photograph we'd had taken on that morning. Dada had a fierce look on his face, but he looked so handsome in his uniform and she, beside him, showing her good side to the camera. Even so, the picture, in stark monochrome, was an unflattering image, so she thought. It didn't capture her man or his tenderness. But still, it was all she had and it never left her possession until she'd willed him home unharmed.

Mother relived the last tender moments of their parting: every word, every promise made. She was to follow William to Orkney and let the family take Dada's place as their provider. It was the one promise she had no intention of keeping - she'd stay in Wick and will Dada to come back undamaged, the same man that she'd loved for the last desperate time just hours before. She'd work and, with a little help from the Lord above, she'd manage.

Help came in the form of Tam MacKay. He would pull strings for her, get her rations and get milk for me. He arranged a cleaning job for her at the council department where he worked and permission to park her wagon in the council grounds. Without him she would have soon failed to keep the promise she'd made to herself and would have left for Orkney and carried on her tinker's life as if nothing at all had happened.

I was growing fast and was a favourite of the husband-less women round about, so it's said, who had formed a bond of support for each other. This hadn't been their first reaction to my mother. At first she had been scorned as the tinker woman the runaways had left behind, by a mealy-mouthed crone who spat out her venom to all who'd listen, branding her a breeder of cowards and praising the Lord that she had only produced two. Mother had taken the woman by the throat, choking her into a dead faint, putting her in the hospital, with the marks of her hands leaving a scarlet bruise and the woman without a voice. Tam was called and found her and me in the jail. The explanation she gave him for her anger caused red faces and apologies and, from then on, my mother was never alone.

Meanwhile, Jonno had been taken into the local school and was beginning to show the first signs of learning.

'Dada would be so proud of ye,' Mother would say when he produced a new word or recited his times table. This was the miracle Mother craved for me too. She loved the wild country, the purple mountains and the clear burns that tumbled down the hillside as much as Dada, but times were changing for everyone. You couldn't just wander from place to place and expect to live off the land with two bairns to keep. She wanted more for us than a tinker's life and she knew that, in his heart, Dada would want the same.

Dada didn't like to talk about the war, but he said that we all learn both good and bad lessons from life and wars were, unfortunately, part of life and we shouldn't shirk from facing the truth. So he would tell it as it really was. How he was reduced to the same coldness that war inflicts on all who take part, willingly or otherwise. We would get small extracts that we didn't understand at the time but his message of man's inhumanity to man came across loud and clear. His description of the battlefield was such that I can still visualise it as clearly as if I'd been there. He told how five-footers went over the top time and again, into the no-man's land that separated the two forces, their task being, before every advance, to silence the snipers' guns and locate and destroy machine-gun nests.

'Ah, Geordie, I tell ye boy,' Dada would say, 'we were covered from head to foot in thick grey mud and we'd slide forward on our bellies, trying to pick our way through the tangle of barbed wire that separated us from the enemy trenches. The glaring lights of the shells bursting overhead to light up the killing zone for all to see, followed rapidly by the whine of bullets filling the air. I'd close my ears against the cries of the wounded and would lay still like the dead, waiting for the exploding shells to extinguish themselves in the grey stinking mud, throwing us once again into an even deeper blackness. The eerie silence that followed was the signal to charge and those of us remaining did just that, screaming hideously as we went. 'The Ladies from Hell' we'd been christened, with our kilts flying, setting the enemy to flight. Geordie, we would gain another twenty yards but at a terrible cost. I heard terrible stories, boy: of men dying slowly and in agony, drowning inside from shells not spraying shrapnel but a silent green cloud of poison gas that killed effortlessly and indiscriminately and of the grey bog that swallowed up the corpses by the thousand.'

There was no rest from the horrors he was witnessing. Scarred in his mind at the senseless carnage, he became a very different man. If he survived this, he knew he'd never be able to resume the nomadic and peaceful life. Deep in his heart, he knew that his travelling days were over. Dada said that he prayed long and hard for the end to come, hoping the last few yards gained at the expense of several companions may be the last he would ever have to endure.

'On November 11th, 1918,' he said, 'an armistice was called and 'the war to end all wars' was over. We'd been relieved and were falling back and, before we could rejoin the front, the gruesome nightmare was over. The relief, Geordie, was unbelievable and that night the survivors got uncontrollably drunk and remained so for almost two days. I was lame from the boots that hadn't been off in weeks. The fear of swollen feet had persuaded me to let well alone. Now I ceremoniously cut them off, peeling the leather away and the skin with it. It would be weeks before I could walk again and my feet would need daily dressing. It was then that the thoughts previously locked in my mind, kept safe from the pollution of the death and destruction all around, came flooding back. Your mother, little Jonno and you, Geordie, put the smile back on my face, that had been absent for almost four years. It was back now and it felt good.'

'Good news travels fast and bad news even faster,' were the words of comfort Tam gave to my mother on the day that the news of victory broke. Cheering crowds waved flags and bonnets and many queued for news of loved ones and read the lists posted daily of deaths and 'missing believed dead'. Tam told how he scanned the list for Dada's name while Mother waited, our photo clutched in her hand and with fear and trepidation stalking her heart. Through the 'Macs' Tam's finger slid, uncovering the alphabetical place for McPhee. When no McPhees listed that day Mother could cling to hope for another twenty-four hours. Tam said he wrote down our name so that she could memorise what it looked like then she could recognise it and scan the list herself in future.

'He'll be back,' she would say to anyone who doubted her. She had willed it and she dared anyone to put his name on that list.

The soldiers came dribbling back, their scars visible for all to see: the physically wounded, the limb-less and sightless, and also the mentally crushed, unrecognisable in themselves, all to their waiting families. Mother scanned the remnants of the once proud army that had marched away, she waited, day after day, watching the wretched show pass by, weeping for the shattered dreams of the women who welcomed back half a man or half a mind, wondering if and when Dada would come. She would shake with anger at the waste of the young men and with the frustration of not knowing where he was, or if he was coming home at all.

'It was several months later,' Mother said, 'April I remember, when the spring breeze was fresh and clean and the trout were there for the tickling. My hope had faded but I dared not give up - giving up would be a sure sign that your Dada was dead. I went to the station every day and scanned the sea of faces, the shell-shocked and the wounded in mind. Would I welcome a pale imitation of the man I remembered? If I had to, I would. Even a shadow of your father, Geordie, would be gratefully accepted.' She told me that she would never forget the moment when the siren blasted out announcing yet another troop train. Nor would she forget the sound of the pipes that led the remnants of the Argyles when they marched up from the railway station as proud as they had been when they marched away.

'I saw your Dada come and what a sight he was, unshaven and ragged, but I blessed all the tinker gods in heaven for sparing his life for us. And if he wanted to travel, then that's what we'd do, I'd not ask him to make another sacrifice, not for me and not for you boys.'

Mother said that I had screamed at the raggy man, who held me aloft and kissed me and, with tears running freely down his face, swore an oath never again to leave us. I had been told stories of Dada by mother and Jonno, and I had formed a picture in my mind of the giant they had painted, so it was some surprise to me to see this little man, inches shorter than mother though twice as broad with a fierce look on his face and to be told to call him 'Dada.' His gentle manner soon won me over and, although it felt strange, I felt instinctively safe in his hands. They had loved that night with a passion to wipe away the past, and she conceived her third child in the explosion of their love.

Mother made no mention of the future but it was clear, Dada said, that he'd come back to a different world than the one he'd left and to a woman who had no real desire to up sticks and go. Mother had survived almost four years without him and had carved out a place for us despite the hostility all around. At times she'd been hungry and desperate, she told me how she'd tried to tickle the trout and had lain down with her hand in the icy brook for what seemed an eternity and finally, with her dress stiff and her hand frozen from the cold, she'd had to walk away empty handed. Jonno had proved our saviour, she said proudly. He'd put into practice what he'd learned from Dada and kept our bellies full with his snares and egg collecting.

'Aye, there's room enough for school books, Geordie,' Dada said, 'but ye canny eat them when yer hungry.'

So, as pleased as Dada was at Jonno's new ability to write his name and read it back, Dada was prouder of Jonno's tinker skills in filling our bellies in his absence.

'From what yer mother says, Geordie, you'll be a scholar boy and that's something I never thought ti see,' he said to me.

Dada conceded it was time for change - but not all at once. He'd always be a tinker and proud of it, but he had made my mother a promise in the trenches - to stay put if that's what she wanted and to let us have our own 'new world.'

'Just one last trek,' he asked, as a farewell to our family's ways. So they took Jonno and me out of school and set off for home to see Dada's old mother and visit his Dada's grave and, that done, we'd join this new world.

We travelled next morning along with Tam, after a night in the

Highlander, where everyone got hopelessly drunk and, while under the influence, Dada's story was released in a torrent of self-recrimination. He'd killed to survive and wasn't proud of what he'd become or what he'd done in the name of King and Country, but still he said, 'I'd do the same again, if it meant getting home unscathed.' Tam nodded his understanding as they carried Dada from the pub to the wagon, singing, partially cleansed of the burden of truth.

Mother watched Dada closely because the darkness brought with it a host of demons. She, bless her, would have to hold him tight and wrestle to keep him from his terrible nightmares. He'd yell and scream abuse as he charged the enemy trenches in his mind, his arms flailing and her dodging his flying fists. My own sweet mother said she hardly recognised the wild man in her bed as the same gentle man who played and taught me during the daylight hours. Tam had warned her, while she waited impatiently for Dada's return, that she might not recognise him as the same man who'd marched away with head held high, and that, if she was lucky enough to get her husband back in one piece, it wouldn't be without a price to pay. She would have to nurse him through recurring hell, it was expected of her.

Back out among the mountains and purple heather, Dada was truly home and it helped heal the mental scars. Finally, after a month of wretched nightmares, he was able to sleep with only the occasional outburst. We took our time meandering slowly toward the west, enjoying the good weather and the peace and quiet that Dada said he had almost forgotten existed. Jonno and I went to school up there. Dada resumed Jonno's education in the tinker ways, but after school hours were done and now with me trailing behind, picking up points along the way.

Mother began to show the first signs of pregnancy. Bouts of early morning sickness alerted Dada and she was forced to tell that the four of us would soon be five and that the wagon and the tent combined wouldn't be big enough to sleep us all. Sorry as she was, she concluded that, on our return to Wick, we would have to think about finding something more suitable to live in. Dada accepted the situation calmly, as he always did, all he said on the matter, was that we must make this last trip one to remember and then, if we were to become townies, so be it.

The greeting we received on our arrival was wild and enthusiastic. All Dada's brothers and sisters were there with their families and he was hailed as a foolish hero and pumped by the men for his story of the 'war to end all wars.' Jonno and I were allowed to sit in and we squatted, either side of Dada, in front of the roaring fire as the men told their stories of dodging the King's draft-catchers, and a roar greeted each successful encounter while the whisky jug took a pass around before the next.

'The war never feckin' started for me, boy,' Will shouted, amending his language slightly for our sake. 'If I want a fight, I can always be sure to get one, any Saturday night, in any camp I choose to get drunk in.'

This was followed by a roar and another pass of the bottle. Jonno tried to take his turn with the whisky but Dada would have none of it.

'We, that is meself and Elizabeth,' Will continued, 'left Wick in a hurry that early dawn, just as the mist was rising, I was still raging in me mind at ye for staying, Rabbie. I don't think me mind was concentrated as well as usual and so I didn't notice our pursuers until we reached the rise at Latheron Hill. It was herself who saw them come, bless her heart.

We counted six on horseback, with a scout out front. I tell ye no lie, a feckin' tinker scout no less, sniffing the trail like a scabby hound. He wore the kilt of our clan and that riled me up all the more. He would have a good knowledge of where we were heading, so I made me mind up there and then to screw his scrawny neck first chance I got - unless Elizabeth beat me to it with her ladle.

We laid up for them and jumped them, smacking their horses' rear ends with the briar and causing havoc. I dragged two of them down, while me dear wife swung her ladle like a meat axe. We left them minus their clothes as we'd promised, with their papers clamped between the cheeks of their arse. As for the traitorous scout, if he has a mind to pass wind, then he'll have to remove the King's shilling first.'

Jonno was laughing uncontrollably now, so I joined him, though the picture I had in my mind would not have done his story justice. When the cheering and laughing and the passing of the jug had finished, Uncle Will took up the tale in a more sober tone.

'We came looking for ye, Rabbie,' he said, 'me and Elizabeth. We had to tie me mother to her wagon wheel to stop her taking on the whole bloody British army. I had to leave the army to my Elizabeth, as they were still holding an unreasonable grudge against those of us who'd absconded. I hid myself in the wagon and peered through a knot-hole to watch the whole thing. Created hell, she did, threatening to brain them all with her ladle and make love, tinker style, to the last one still standing, until he'd beg to be back with the

Germans. She frightened the shit out of all of them, bless her. Said they'd kidnapped her husband for the army and if they didn't give him back, she'd take one of them to keep her going until they did.'

I was losing interest now but was reluctant to leave the fire.

William continued, 'Elizabeth eyed them all, like a Collie-dog eyeing the sheep, and grabbed the smallest by the neck. 'Is it to be me husband or him?' says she, shaking the unfortunate by his shirt front. Their commanding officer explained, after consulting his list, that it was too late, the Argyles had been shipped out that morning. 'The King's claimed him, madam,' he said in a snotty English voice, 'and I'm very much afraid, you can't have him either,' he said, rescuing the young soldier from her grip. She grabbed him, the commanding officer, brass buttons and all and head butted him like a stag, broke his nose as clean as a whistle.'

A huge cheer went up around the fire and William's face creased into a fond smile.

'We left without saying thank you, or kiss my arse, now aren't we the heathens, boy? Your Sarah, though, wouldn't leave either, try as we may to persuade her. That brave little girl stuck it out there amongst all the resentment and waited for ye, even got herself thrown in jail, so I heard.'

The jug passed around again, loosening Dada's tongue and, for the first time, he gave vent to his pent-up feelings. 'I've seen some real bastards in action Will and I've been no better meself, God forgive me. I'll always regret sinking so low. I walked away so proud in me fancy kilt, with me pride pumping me up to twice me normal size. But I crawled back with me tail tucked firmly between me legs and hardly able to look ye all in the eye. Now all I have left is the smell of gangrenous stumps in me nose and I wake at night gagging at the mustard gas floating unseen on the breeze and listening to the cries of better men, bayoneted and left to die in the rat-infested trenches. There were heroes there all right, boy, but they died first.'

'Survival is king, Rabbie boy.' Uncle Will said. 'Dead heroes are just as dead, now forget all that nonsense and pass the jug, and we'll cleanse your mind with the amber nectar. He wrapped his huge arms around Dada and gave him a hug, blinking away the tears. He was followed one at a time by all the brothers.

Dada asked where their mother lay and Will led us to her grave to pay our respects.

'Ah, Rabbie, she took the news that her youngest had been taken very badly, boy, and she ladled me good for not stopping ye. She was miserable then and all through the next year, unable to write the words and knowing ye'd never be able to read them if she could. So she willed her strength to ye, her thoughts to ye and her love to ye boy. And one year almost to the day ye left, she died. I made her a promise on her deathbed that our offspring would at least learn to write the words.'

They all congregated around the graveside, swaying, crying and drunk from the whisky, where Dada confessed to his mother's grave the depths of his misery in the darkest days in France. He'd felt her strength reach out to him when he was almost at his wit's end. She'd pumped iron into his veins and given him the will to survive.

'Your message of the mind, I want ye ti know, dear mother, it found its mark,' and they all said 'amen' to that.

We slept in the camp that night and it was my first and only experience of sleeping in the wild, though one I'll never forget. The morning saw a continuation of the story-telling and drinking, while the women gossiped relentlessly about townsfolk and their mealy-mouthed ways. Elizabeth wanted to know how Sarah and Dada could put up with their prissy-arsed snobbery without breaking a few teeth.

'They look down on ye, it's true,' Mother said, 'and murmur about ye when yer back's turned, but my Robbie insisted that wagging tongues canny hurt ye, unless ye let them, so for the sake of the children's schooling, we put up with it.'

'He's a saint, that man of yours,' they all agreed.

'My bugger,' Elizabeth had said, 'would have been in jail long since.' They all nodded, saying their headstrong husbands were all cast in the same mould and that Dada must have sucked all the goodness from his mother's tit and left the rest to scrat and squabble for the remainder and that they'd been scratting ever since. At this point Jonno whispered to me that it was time to sneak off, so we left Dada and the family howling and passing the bottle to and fro and went in search of something to do. We came face to face with a scraggy-looking hound peering at us from under a trailer.

'Uhh! He's the ugliest dog I've ever seen,' whispered Jonno, 'and he stinks like he's shit himself.' Jonno held his nose.

The dog seemed to take our conversation as encouragement and, as we walked on, he followed us.

'The bugger stinks worse than ye, Geordie,' Jonno said, pushing him away with his foot, but the dog took this as a game and grabbed Jonno's foot in a playful game of tug-a-war. 'Get him off me, Geordie, hit him over the head with your boot, then perhaps he'll bugger off and leave us to breathe, and don't ye start going soft on him. He's a filthy hound and he stinks like a hog.'

The dog let go and looked at us, waiting for the next part of the game to begin.

'Just ignore him and he'll go away,' Jonno whispered. But he didn't, and his smell was making us feel sick. Wherever we went the poor creature was just a stride behind us.

'Let's take him to the river and give him a bath, Jonno.'

'Okay, but if we're ti give him a bath, we'll need a rope.'

I dragged a rope from under the trailer and we ran off towards the river with the dog loping after us.

'He's not going to like this bathing, Geordie. You're going to have to wade across with a rope on him and pull him in after ye, and I'll stay here with the other rope, to stop him climbing out the other side, how's that?'

'Why me?'

'Cause it was your idea, and he likes you and seems to trust you, so he's sure to follow.' Jonno cut the rope in two equal pieces and tied both to his neck, giving one to me and holding firmly on to the other. The hound gave us a mournful look, suspended as he was between the pair of us, as if he was about to meet his maker.

'You'd better go, Geordie.'

I usually did what Jonno said, but the water was cold and I hesitated. But I knew Jonno wouldn't go, so I had to give in.

'I'll go for the poor dog, Jonno, and not just because ye say so.'

I stripped off, tied the rope around my waist and waded slowly into the water, pulling the hound after me. Jonno held the other line and fed it out slowly, keeping the yelping dog held fast between the two of us, letting the fast-flowing river do the washing. The river was icy cold from the mountain snow, and, hampered by the thrashing hound and the deepening water, I was soon bowled over, slipping on the smooth pebbles that coated the river bed. I remember to this day the feel of the icy water rushing over me and of splashing my way toward the far bank, huffing and puffing at the blood-freezing cold.

The dog was now halfway and could go no further, being held by Jonno's line. I was still in the water and beginning to turn blue, when Jonno called 'time' and let the dog make the far bank. I finally crawled out but now was in no fit state to go back. I hadn't given a thought to how my clothes would follow me and now my jaw was aching with the chattering of my teeth.

'Ye'd better come on back, Geordie,' Jonno shouted, seeing my uncontrollable shivering, but I was shaking so badly that I couldn't answer him.

'Hold on to the dog then, boy and I'll pull ye back, Jonno shouted, beginning to panic. 'Come on, Geordie.' The anxiety was now showing in his voice.

I clung on, I don't know how, to the swimming dog and was dragged, shaking and shivering and barely conscious, through the icy water and up the bank. Jonno said later that he started to massage the feeling back into my numb arms and legs, dressing me while I shook fit to bust. Jonno lay on top of me. He told me later that he felt the cold creep into his own body and how Dada had once laid old Jen down and snuggled up against her in a blizzard to beat the cold. Thank the Lord, Jonno never forgot a tinker trick. He called to the dog, who came with a wagging tail and patted the ground beside my prostrate body. The dog shook the water from his coat and sat down obediently. Huddled together they breathed some life back into my shivering body. The first sign of life, Jonno told me, was the sound of coughing from somewhere beneath the hair of the dog.

'What have ye done to me prize hound?' Will asked as we wandered back, 'and what's wrong with little Geordie? He's shaking fit to bust.'

'We thought to give the hound a bath, he stunk so bad and Geordie fell in the river.'

'A good massage,' Will said, 'and a drop of the amber nectar's what he needs by the look of him.'

I was carried off to get one of Aunt Elizabeth's famous warmers. By the time she was finished, I was hot, embarrassed and half drunk - but revived.

'Where did you get such a scabby-looking hound, Uncle?' Jonno wanted to know.

'Ah well, his looks is deceiving, you see. He has the best of both worlds for the betting man, Jonno. He looks mangy and dirty and it's true he stinks to high heaven. It's how I get good odds on him, but he's as fast as the wind when he wants to run. He shows them all his arse when it comes to a race. He's never been headed yet, I call him McDonald, after that mangy clan, and he runs just like them. I'll take ye to a race Jonno, if yer Dada don't take ye back too soon.'

My mother, though, was worried about me, because I was showing the first signs of a fever.

'We have to get him back to Wick, Robbie and quickly.'

She nursed me with tots of whisky to keep the body heat and we started right away. Mother and Dada said their goodbyes to everyone and said that they hoped that they'd understand the need to change and turn away from the travelling life for the children's sake. Dada talked to me as I lay shivering and hallucinating in the cart, mother mopping my face and Jen going at her fastest trot. I was, so they said, boiling one minute and deathly cold the next. Dada's voice floated to me through my semi-conscious fever. I can recall some of the words of encouragement he whispered to me: he told me of the war and of the changes that wars always bring, and about how people were eager to work and build a new life having faced their own mortality.

'Your mother wants ye to have the schooling, boy, and to learn the things I hadn't needed for the natural life we led. So we've decided to give this new life a chance.' After a dash across country to get treatment and courtesy of some string-pulling by Tam Mackay, I was hospitalised. Meanwhile, Dada was allowed to buy an old shack for two hundred pounds on a small piece of ground with space for the wagon and old Jen. It took all his five-years' back-pay from the army, which was bad news, especially with another mouth to feed, but Dada was determined to give us the chance this new world offered.

§

Robert McPhee

Chapter Three

Leaving Home

The first rumblings of a stock market crash in far-off America were appearing in the newspapers and the consequences would affect even the tinker families of the Western Isles. Dada could make little of this and was kept busy making pots and selling them from door to door, while our mother gutted the herring at the harbour between administering potions to me. Wick was now our home and with it came the prejudices of the town dwellers.

'Those untrustworthy, dirty, shifty tinkers,' as one old crone referred to us, 'should be avoided at all cost. Everything has to be put under lock and key, now that the place is open house to tinker families. As likely as not, they'll up and go at a moment's notice - with all your personal property in the back of their wagon.'

My mother caught a group murmuring that it looked like the tinker man was making up for lost time and that she was going to add yet another little brat to her filthy brood.

'Ye soon bloody forgot the courage of my wee tinker man,' Sarah bellowed. 'He was good enough to fight for ye. Now!' she said, drawing her ladle from her bag, 'I'll brain a few for him.'

Dada had to restrain her or her ladle would have visited more damage on the local townswomen. He calmed her down, saying that he'd seen enough fighting to last two lifetimes and she should never respond to idle gossip.

'Wagging tongues canny hurt you, unless you let them, now let that be an end to it.'

But of course, their nasty insinuations were true and Mother was pregnant and it was showing.

Mother knew it was going to be difficult to make ends meet, but she had no room in her for regret. She talked of the freedom of the moors, the mountains and burns, of the sweet taste of fresh trout in the skillet, of the isolation to bathe in the loch and make love in the mountain grass under a cloudless sky.

'How could I have taken all that from ye, Rabbie?' she said. 'God forgive me this time for being the fool.'

She put us first, as all good mothers do, and Dada reminded her of the cold with only the freezing water in winter to bathe in and of how they had buried their own sweet child, my brother, by the loch side.

'She did right, Geordie,' Dada told me later. 'You're a bright little man with your lessons, and if Jonno would stop fighting our battles, he would be too.'

The next five years were the worst in living memory, according to Dada. The very first midwinter, it was cold and the stock-market crash sent a small ripple into the far reaches of the highlands. The news meant little to the poorest inhabitants of Wick, although the effects of the strangling tentacles squeezed what had once been a thriving fishing port, leaving it all but idle. We had always been poor, but the abject poverty that filtered across the nation forced us to raid the fields for carrots or turnips and set the traps for anything we could catch that would fill our bellies.

The Salvation Army depot that had kept us in boots and coats was overrun by people forced to swallow their pride and queue for the handouts. There was no money for Dada's pots and pans nor for odd jobs, and the women queued at the harbour for the herring boats to come, fighting off the seagulls for the fish heads and tails to feed their families. How anyone survived the depression, no one could explain - but we did. Charlie was now five and had been raised almost exclusively on herring scraps and potatoes - 'tatty pie' Mother called it - though to look at him you would never know it. He had her beautiful auburn hair and olive skin and Dada's blue eyes.

Deprivation can turn children into nasty, angry yobs and we faced this anger every day at school. The local boys would single us out and we would fight, together or alone. Jonno needed no excuse to batter some up-and-comer who thought to insult his tinker heritage. I was never so quarrelsome and would avoid trouble if I possibly could but, if I was pushed into defending Jonno or Charlie, I'd fight like a demon and leave my teeth marks for all to see. Even Charlie, on his first day, came home with a black eye. Once Jonno was ringed in the playground, the local bully taunting him and saying everybody knew that his mother was a scrubber who churned out little bastards like a rabbit on heat - he'd heard his mother say so. He crowed all this to the surrounding boys. Jonno asked four boys in the surrounding circle but no one would chance telling him what a scrubber was and what Mother had in common with rabbits on heat. He turned finally to the bully who'd said it, and rewarded him with a punch in the mouth and one less tooth to worry about cleaning - just in case it was an insult.

The isolation this prejudice forced on us encouraged a bond of loyalty and we likened ourselves to the storybook heroes Tam once described to us, from the stories of Alexander Dumas. We became known as the Three Musketeers and if one of us was in trouble, the others would come running - Charlie to roar encouragement and me as back up, though sometimes to weigh in with a punch. The fighting kept Jonno satisfied most days of the week and his face was never free of new cuts to add to the old scars that littered his skin.

He could account for each and every one. At night, squashed together in our single bed, Jonno would paint a bloodthirsty picture of his encounters, embellishing events for Charlie's sake. Charlie would be asked to select one scar and Jonno would tell the story behind it. He carried them proudly like badges of honour. I had scars too but was less proud of them, and my stories were of a more conventional kind. Charlie would turn his nose up at them, preferring the way Jonno righted the injustices of life with his fists. Jonno grew to hate schooling and townies, he longed to return to the solitary travelling life. He became an unruly and disruptive influence, prompting his teacher to write to Dada.

'I've got a feckin note for Dada, Geordie, from that old bastard McNab. He never did like me. He called me a hoolihan, whatever that is.'

'It's hooligan and it means you're out of control,' I said.

'He picks on me 'cause we're tinkers, boy and he thinks he's better than us.'

'Ye have to make an effort, Jonno. Ye have to learn to read and write, then they'll look up to ye and not because ye can knock seven shades of shit out of them.'

'I can tickle a trout right into my hand, Dada showed me and I can make a snare to catch our dinner, set a fire, read the signs of the wild, make tinker stew with leaves and roots growing wild by the loch, that's more than he can do.'

'Aye, but can ye read a book all the way through, Jonno? Or write a sentence that says what you mean it to say?'

'Which would you prefer to know, Charlie, tinker ways or schooling?' Jonno asked Charlie.

'Don't ask him, he's already been strapped three times this week for swearing in class.'

'They can shove their words up their arses long ways,' said Charlie.

'Mam and Dada gave up the travelling so we could have some schooling,' I said. 'It's what they want for us, to be able ti read and write.' But I was wasting my time, the tinker was too strong in Jonno, so I let it be.

Tam Mackay had again been summoned to read unwelcome news, this time that it was the teacher's opinion that Jonno McPhee was not a suitable candidate for their school and, if his behaviour couldn't be amended, he would have to be expelled. Dada discussed with Tam whether Jonno wouldn't be better suited returning to a life with his family on the Western Isles.

'They'll never educate the traveller out of him, however much schooling he gets,' Dada said. It was true that Jonno looked forward eagerly to meeting and being with the family when they came for the herring catch. He revelled in the stories Uncle William told of McDonald's racing exploits and would repeat them to us at every opportunity. The dog had won many bets, due to the bony, scraggy look of him, but, as his reputation grew, his opponents had grown more wary.

'I attempted to disguise the hound, Jonno,' Will said, 'by staining his coat red with berries from the briar, but ah,' he sighed, 'ye canny disguise his speed. So finally, despite all me best efforts, he had to be withdrawn and as ye well know, once a racing dog has served his purpose, he's no use to man nor beast. Everything must pay its way Jonno, no passengers.'

'But McDonald was good for you, Uncle Will,' Jonno pleaded.

'There's no room for sentiment in tinker life, boy. Once their usefulness comes to an end, so does their life. Though, in his case, I've made an exception, I've decided to put McDonald to stud and hope an offspring will inherit his looks and his speed.'

Jonno was satisfied with the compromise and he absorbed the tinker education eagerly. Contrasting it with the dull book-learning methods of his school, it was no contest.

I was coming toward my ninth birthday and Mother said I had the handsome good looks and the raven black hair of my father. She said I was different, I was the only one of us who loved school. The learning of reading and writing was opening up a whole new world to me, a world that had been closed to me and my family. I didn't really remember the travelling life that Jonno enjoyed and I was happy to learn and behave like the other town children. And something more, she said, set me apart.

'Ye have the pride, and will measure your own step and follow no one, Geordie.'

Charlie, on the other hand, although only five, had styled himself in Jonno's image. Jonno was Charlie's hero, he'd learned to scrap and swear just like him. With auburn ringlets and the blue eyes of an angel, he was a deceptively innocent-looking child - until he laid his hobnail into his tormenter.

'Never back down,' Jonno told him, 'or it will be the worse for ye and if ye have to take a beating, then so be it.'

Dada put it to Mother, though with a tear in his eye.

'It seems sensible to let Jonno have his freedom. He was born into it and he'd be happier with Will and Elizabeth, if we let him choose. School's not for him and now that we're five it would ease the family's burden. Tam and I think it will be the best for him and we'll see him whenever he's visiting. I've made up me mind now, so best have your say and be done with it.'

Mother, for the first time in her life, reared up on him.

'Ye and Tam MacKay have decided to give my first-born away, have ye? Well, ye can bloody well think on, Robbie boy. I'll work harder and he can have my share of the necessary. I'll pass on the second-hand clothes, from Jonno to Geordie and on to little Charlie. Boots only need to be worn in winter and in school. They could take them off outside to make them last.'

She ranted for half an hour on the economies she'd make, while Dada sat quietly. He said that he was proud of the way she fought for her family, but he knew it would be his decision and that it would be for the best.

Jonno had taught Charlie to swear like a trooper and when Charlie was angry he would come out with a mouthful of shameful words. Charlie was devastated at the news of his hero's departure and suggested to Mother that I would be a much better choice and, that night, Mother cried herself to sleep in Dada's arms. But, by dawn, she was ready to give up her first-born. Dada would pass the word on through the grapevine, though with a heavy heart, and await the reply.

Dada broke the news to us all gently, that Jonno would have to leave, for just a wee while, to live with William and Elizabeth on the Western Isles.

'School's not for ye, boy, yer a tinker born and it's in yer blood,' he told Jonno.

Jonno tried to speak through the tears that sprung from his stubborn face and his lips quivered as he stuttered that he wanted to stay. He admitted that he loved the tinker life, but he loved his Dada and mother more and he could change if change was needed.

'You, boy, are like yer grandfather - too wild for change and if shackled by town rules, ye'd be destined for trouble. I'll miss ye, boy,' Dada said, hugging Jonno to him and the tears ran down our faces.

'Me ain hands brought ye screaming into this world,' Dada continued, 'and now I've got to let ye go, for your ain sake and to ease the burden on the family. Remember yer tinker pride, boy, and take with ye the love of me and yer mother - it'll give ye the strength, as my mother willed her strength to me in the Great War. Go see yer mother now and make it easier for her by being strong.'

'We were a team, Dada, in our roving days. I'll always remember that's what ye said,' said Jonno.

'You'll be a team too, you and Will, he'll bring you back to see us whenever he's passing.'

A month later, a delighted William met with Dada and agreed to wait just outside of town, whilst Dada and Mother said their goodbyes to Jonno then Dada would send the boy to him.

'William, ye treat him right, boy, or ye'll have me to answer to.'

'I will, he's family, our first, and Elizabeth'll spoil him, seeing as she hasn't one of her ain. I'll give him a good and free tinker life.

It's been good enough for ye and it'll be good enough for Jonno.'

Dada's eyes filled, as we watched Jonno go.

'Away now, boy,' he said softly and come ye back a man by the winter and see yer old Dada.'

He knew this was the tinker way, his own mother had hired off his brothers before he'd been born, but it hurt to let Jonno go. They'd shared so much. We watched him go and it broke our hearts. Dada took us out, he heard Sarah stifle a painful cry when Jonno said his farewells. Charlie, though, tucked the sadness of Jonno's leaving under his cap and took over where his hero had left off. It was all I could do to keep him from following down the same road. Meanwhile, Mother added to the family like a mother hen and produced another egg to replace the one stolen from the family basket. Dada hadn't the heart to deny her and so, in the midst of the depression, we were again restored to five. And baby Hughie was followed closely by a sixth, a girl named Jean, after my mother's sister, and the same problem again reared its ugly head worse than ever. Although the depression was slowly abating, Dada's earnings still wouldn't stretch to the growing demands of the larger family. Dada explained, argued and comforted Mother, who just couldn't see the need to lose another son.

'The oldest must fly the nest my girl, it's all we can do. It's Geordie's turn to make way for the youngsters. He can be hired out like my brothers were and we'll see him all the time. He'll have to finish with school and work for his keep on one of the local farms.'

This news came as a devastating blow. I loved school and was a good student. Representations from my teachers were testament to my ability and I pleaded to be allowed to stay. Dada was proud that

I'd flown in the face of the surrounding prejudice and had shown that I could rise above it, given the chance. He said he would dearly love to give me the opportunity, but his hands were securely tied: I'd have to go to a local farm when the school term ended for the summer break and that, God forgive him, was a fact.

My work at the farm would be long and hard, and would begin in earnest with the harvest. I said my tearful goodbyes and promised to write and visit, if I was allowed out. Dada said my leaving was a harder cross for him to bear than Jonno's because at least Jonno had family and was living the life he enjoyed. (He had returned the following winter from his tinker life, and was a changed boy -resourceful, capable and strong, and leading the life he was born to.)

Now it was my turn and I left with an overwhelming burden of sadness, cut off from my schooling, cheated of the knowledge I craved and with a feeling that I'd been sold into slavery. Dada had explained that difficult times needed difficult solutions but that I should keep my dream locked in my head to comfort me through the hard times to come, and God-willing, some day I would fulfil my dream.

'Don't let it go, boy. You're different. Ye have more in you than a tinker life could offer. I had a dream too,' he confessed, 'not like yours but a dream just the same. The Great War spoiled me, boy, took the heart from me. Ye must get away from Wick at your first opportunity and never look back.'

I'd never had such a meaningful conversation with Dada before. I'd always felt Jonno was closer to him, loving the tinker life as he did. It hadn't entered my head that Dada had once had a dream, he'd been just Dada, a proud little tinker man getting by as best he could, with a love of the wild natural things that had been his world. Now I knew that I was my father's son and that I must get away for the sake of both of us and see where my dream would lead me. For now, though, I must earn my keep and wait for an opportunity to come and when it did, I'd have to be brave enough to grab it.

I went to my mother, as Jonno had, my emotions held in check, determined to ease the pain I'd see in her eyes. Her tears these days seemed to flow given the slightest opportunity. She was alone and sitting in her nursing chair, muttering her sins to the Almighty. She patted the seat beside her for me to sit and began to apologise for failing me and breaking the promise she'd made at my birth.

'Don't, Mammy.'

She waved me to silence,

'I promised before God that life for ye would be different, we'd stop travelling and you'd have your education. I'm sorry, ye deserve better.'

'Mam, I was getting bored at school and I like farm work. I'll be right enough, you'll see. I won't stop reading. Ye started me off on the right road and I thank ye for it, I'll not stop till I have an education or a trade. I'll try to make your promise come true, so wish me well and keep an eye out for Charlie. Say goodbye to Hughie and Jeannie for me,' I said, putting on a brave face.

Tam MacKay came over to say his goodbyes and it was plain to see that he thought it a sorry thing that my education was to be sacrificed, though, truth to tell, he had no alternative to offer, just some advice which I would prize, it would stay with me and comfort me in my lowly hours. He'd shed his tinker life and become a wiser man for it and he wanted me to know the power of education.

'There is no worse poverty than poverty of the mind, Geordie, so read on and think on, that costs nothing. Never sink to the raggy-arsed level and don't try to blot disappointment out with drink. When you close your eyes at night, just dream of a better place, where some day you'll put poverty behind ye.'

§

Robert McPhee

Chapter Four

Maggie Crook Penny-a-Look

I could hear my mother's pitiful wail as I left, my boots swinging from my neck, tears streaming down my face and some bread and jam in my sack. I rushed headlong up the coast road toward God knows what, scared and alone for the first time in my life. My mind was darting from one extreme to the other like a moth flirting with fiery disaster. I reflected that just a few days ago I was at school and secure in the body of my family and now, as if by some cruel trick of fate, I was to work for my keep, surrounded by strangers.

Trepidation walked with me, as I made my way up the track leading to McDonald's farm. It was already getting dark when I splashed my way across the yard to the kitchen door, starting the dogs barking. I'd been past on errands for my mother and so knew Angus McDonald by sight, also by reputation from the kids at school who'd hired out in the holidays. They said he was a dour, unsmiling scrooge of a man. As I stood there, hoping by some miracle that all this was a mistake and that I would be packed off home with a flea in my ear, a woman answered the door. Her appearance gave me a sinking feeling and I could see she was as unimpressed with me as I was with her.

'You'll be Geordie McPhee then,' Aggie McDonald sniffed.

Her first words, or more the way she sniffed, confirmed my feeling that this was a place where humour was a rare commodity.

'I hope yer stronger than ye look, boy, or ye won't earn yer keep.

Ye'll find a place in the barn and some sacks to cover ye. Breakfast is at six, If ye sleep in, ye'll go without till dark. Away then, boy and I hope yer worth it.'

The barn was a small structure with bales of hay stacked from floor to rafters, some rusty equipment and holes in the roof covered by flapping sheets. I sat in the straw and ate my jam sandwiches then I made myself a place to lie down. The barn was home to everything that crawled and the warmth of my body was like a magnet to them, I spent my first night in fitful bouts of sleeping and scratching and wondering what in the world I'd done to deserve to be here. My head was spinning at my change of fortune as I waited for the morning.

I seemed finally to sleep, until the cockerel at the foot of my bed crowed me awake and I rubbed my eyes. I could hear movement coming from the yard outside. I crawled to the wall and peered through the gaps. The light was murky, as it is just before the dawn breaks, but I could just make out Angus McDonald as he washed his thin body under the tap in the yard. He was huffing and puffing as the icy cold water swilled from his scrawny neck down his back and dripped from the cheeks of his elephant's arse.

This didn't seem to help his humour and he yelled 'Boy!' at the top of his voice.

I almost burst through the wall of the barn in my haste not to inflame his temper further and presented myself before him, awaiting the first order of the day.

'Ah, there ye are. Weell dinny just stand there, fetch me a towel from the kitchen drawer yonder,' he pointed. 'And hurry on before I freeze ti death.'

He said it as if it were my fault he hadn't brought it with him in the first place. I was to learn very quickly that all things, from foul weather to the lack of eggs from the hens, would somehow have something to do with me. I was a Jonah and he cursed every morning that he'd agreed to have me and that he must be getting fuddled to take on a tinker boy. It was well known, he would rant, that all tinkers were wasters and would steal the fillings from yer teeth, if ye were silly enough to sleep with yer mouth open.

I agreed with all this by nodding my head after each statement, or shaking it in disbelief at the wickedness of the tinkers and tutting that they'd sneak in like thieves in the night and rob him blind.

I wondered why on earth he had agreed to hire me on. I found out much later from Aggie that Angus thought that one favour to the tinkers may be repaid by letting him and his stock alone. I could have told him, though I dare not, that there was no such honour among tinkers.

Once we had his gripes out of the way, he wasn't so bad. The work was hard, the milking first and feeding the stock then away to the fields for the real work. I wielded a sickle throughout the day and learned to tie the shafts of corn and stack them in large mounds to await Aggie with the horse and cart. I fell asleep on the ride home on that first day and tumbled into my hay bed too tired to come in for tea. I think I pleased Angus right well, because his tone towards me changed—even Aggie called me Geordie.

Why wouldn't they be pleased? I thought. I'd worked like a slave and it hadn't as much as cost them a dinner.

As the days passed I could reflect on my new life and think how Jonno may have responded to these two slave drivers. I knew, of course, he would have run off after helping himself to anything he could carry just to teach them a lesson. 'So why hadn't I then?' I argued with myself. 'I'm cast in the same mould.' Even little Charlie would have stood in defiance. My obedience annoyed me, but I realised my father had known that I was the one who would keep his end of the bargain.

I followed Angus from job to job, mending a gate, repairing the barn wall and as I watched him turn his hand to anything, I began to learn the rudiments of the carpentry trade. It was interesting and tired as I was after a day in the fields, I would look forward to the time we'd spend doing the odd jobs.

The working week ended and was followed by a Sunday morning attendance at a small kirk, after our morning chores were done. There I was obliged to sing hymns and give thanks for God's bounty and the McDonald's charity.

These were hard days, but learning to use tools and the satisfaction in making and mending, with anything we could find, kept me from deserting in my darker hours. Angus was too tight to spend a penny on replacements for anything so I learned to make do and mend. This wasn't the education I had hoped for, but it would be useful, of that I was certain.

At night I missed my family and the feeling of abandonment would come back to haunt me. Alone, tired and hungry, or when my hands were cut from the corn stalks with no one to care if they stung. Or if it rained and I was working wet through to the skin with no time to get dry, shivering in my hay bed until morning.

At times like these, I admit, I cried for my mother's love.

It was early one Sunday morning, I was milking a stubborn old heifer named Jezebel. She seemed to have taken a dislike to me, why I had no idea. She'd make life as difficult as possible by thrashing me around the head with her tail and trying her best to kick the bucket or anything else she could reach. I'm not sure if she was ticklish or if she just didn't like the feel of my fingers round her private parts but, whatever the reason, the feeling was mutual. I had almost finished when she lifted her tail and dropped a load on my foot. The heat from the cow shit was not unpleasant on my cold toes, but the stink stayed with me long after the cold had returned. I squeezed her tit in revenge and she gave me such a look that I'd be wary of crossing a field in case she'd be bearing a grudge.

It was then that I heard my name called faintly from a way off. I scrambled outside and caught a glimpse of old Jen coming up the road with my father sitting on the wagon waving his arm at me. I took off like a startled rabbit across the field and met them at the fence.

'Dada, you've come for me, and where's me mother?'

'I've come to see if you're all right, Geordie, and to bring ye news of the family, but not to bring ye home just yet, boy, not just yet. Yer mother couldn't face ye, boy. She still blames herself, but she told me if ye were hungry or poorly to bring ye back to her, with God's speed. Well, boy, are ye?'

I shook my head and it took a mighty effort so to do. For the life of me I wanted nothing more than to leap on old Jen's back and ride home.

'I'm glad to hear it, Geordie. I brought ye a biscuit yer mother saved for ye and she said to eat it slow or some'll be lost to crumbs.'

I nodded, tears in my eyes.

'You can tell Mam I'm learning a trade and that I can mend

anything and when I do come home, I'll make her a rocker for her nursing chair.'

We chatted and I stroked old Jen's neck. Dada's eyes took in all my body, every scratch and bruise, every torn nail.

'Aye, yer doing good Geordie, but make sure the old skinflint pays ye properly or I'll be knocking his door, tell him.'

I'd never thought to earn wages and I'm sure Angus had happily forgotten, but if that's the bargain they'd struck, then I'd have to draw my pay.

It was my Dada's way of making me stand up and get my worth. I thought about how to approach Angus as I wandered back across the field, chewing on my biscuit, so deep in thought that when I looked up, they were gone.

At tea time we three sat around the table and I had made my mind up that this would be the best time to say my piece. With no crumb left on our plates, I stumbled to my feet, upsetting my chair and startling the pair out of their satisfaction. I had rehearsed over and over to the cockerel in the barn what I would say, keeping his interest by tossing him seed until I was word perfect. The asking, I knew, would've been easy for Jonno and I thought to pretend that I was he. But I had to harden up and this was my first test. With the two hard, scowling faces waiting to snap my request like a trap, I momentarily lost my nerve.

'Weell…laddie?' Angus screeched.

This was one of those learning moments when you sink or swim and I was about to strike out, arms flailing, for adulthood.

'Well, Angus…Mr McDonald,' I stammered, seeing Aggie's look. 'It's about my pay. Ye may have forgotten, but I've been keeping

a tally and to my reckoning it's twenty-six days that ye owe me.'
They were taken by surprise, but no more than I was at my boldness.
It encouraged me and I continued with new confidence. 'And I'd
be obliged if ye'd settle up.'

'Ye'd be obliged, would ye?' he said, raising his bushy white
eyebrows to the heavens and looking for support from Aggie. She
only scowled at me as if I had the cheek of the devil to ask and began
noisily to clear away the dishes.

'Make no mind of the food ye put away, ye little ingrate,' she
threw at me as she left to the washing-up sink. 'Dinny let him bully
ye, Angus.'

I stood my ground, determined as I was and with my hand out,
more because I didn't know what else to do.

'Ah, yer a rumm'n, Geordie, I can see that. Weell,' he whimpered,
'I was going to give ye a little something, because ye've been right
handy.'

It was like tearing his heart out and squeezing the blood from
it, but I'd come this far so I wasn't about to settle for the sixpence
and a few pennies that bounced down from his purse on to the table.

'No, I'd thought four pence a day would be fair,' I said. 'And
at my calculation, that comes to eight shillings and eight pence ye
owe me.'

'What's that ye say!' he screeched with a look of mock horror
showing on his face and taking a sideways glance at Aggie's ramrod
back at the sink.

'Pay the little thief, if yer a skulking coward then,' she snapped
over her shoulder. 'It's more money than ye give me in a month.'

'What about me educating ye in the use of the tools?' Angus

struck back. 'And the food and the board and lodgings ye owe me? Twenty-six days, ye say, is it that long? Weell, of that shall we say a penny for your food, and a penny for educating ye, and a penny for bed and board. So I'll give ye a penny a day as proper payment—that's one pound and sixpence, agreed?'

I'd been outmanoeuvred but had learned a valuable lesson.

I took the money, the first I'd had that truly belonged to me, and resolved to take something home for my mother to show that I was a working man and in good spirits.

My relations with Angus were much improved after our confrontation and I learned later that he loved nothing better than to win an argument, especially one that saved him money. There was, of course, a case for the saved three pence to be handed over to Aggie, as she provided the food, board and lodgings, but this was conveniently forgotten.

The following weeks saw me trusted to small mending jobs and if I say so myself, I made a pretty fair job of them, so I badgered Angus for a rise. We wrangled back and forth as he expected and after the usual struggle, he agreed to pay me extra for each job that he was satisfied I had completed well, at no cost to him, but anything I had to buy was deducted from my pay. The extra work took up most of my evenings and I was fit for nothing but work and sleep. I'd saved my money, feeding it into a tin I'd found behind the barn, which was now becoming so heavy I worried that it was a temptation to any passer-by and set about finding a secure hiding place for it. This was a new experience for me and though I didn't recognise it at the time, I was becoming mercenary and suspicious and would check on my tin whenever I passed the barn. The money was my future and I knew that every penny would count.

I looked forward to each Sunday—it was only a part workday, for the other part we got ourselves smartened up and visited the local church, which proved light relief. To outsiders it appeared that I had 'got religion' and Angus took full credit for reforming his hired tinker boy. I obliged with a smile. It was a Sunday like any other and we'd arrived back at the farm. I made my way to the barn and threw myself down on my hay bed with every intention of counting my savings, when a voice called my name.

'Geordie, Geordie,'

Jonno's head poked round the barn door followed closely by Charlie's. They dived headlong on me, laughing at my scrubbed appearance.

'The old scrooge has turned ye soft, boy,' Jonno taunted.

My new-found work muscles made me a match for the pair and I threw them off.

'Beware,' said I. 'I'm a working man now and I'll take no nonsense from tinkers. Steady now and I'll show ye me wages. Turn yer backs while I get my tin and no peeking. I don't trust tinker boys when it comes to my hard-earned money.'

I showed them my savings, all in shiny penny pieces that half filled the tin.

'He's rich, Charlie. We have a wealthy brother and like a good brother, he's probably going to treat us.'

'Is that right, Geordie?' Charlie beamed.

Nothing could have been further from my mind as I lovingly counted each one back into the tin.

'This was hard-earned, boys. It's me tool money I'm saving for a set of tools and when I'm ready, I'll be back home.'

'When ye go, I'll take yer job on, if ye can earn wages,' Charlie piped up. It was the first time that Charlie had wanted to emulate me, but not the last.

'Well, are ye going to treat us then, Geordie, or are ye going to forget we shared the same bed and fought the same fights?' Jonno asked.

Charlie nodded his head.

'Aye, well I might,' I said.

Still green behind the ears, my Dada would call me, but I was feeling lordly.

There was no backing out now. I'd boasted of my fortune, so now I was caught.

We set off toward the town with my feet scarcely touching the ground, my pockets weighed down with coins and with suggestions of how I could spend my fortune tumbling out thick and fast. I was full of myself as I marched down the coast road, 'the toast of Wick,' they said, 'benefactor of the poor tinker boys.' A hero now to Charlie and respected by Jonno as a shrewd operator, having told how I'd negotiated my pay and squeezed that little bit more from Angus's purse, which we all agreed was a feat nothing short of magic. Shrewd, I thought myself, but in reality I was ripe for the picking.

Straight into McReedie's Sweetie Shop we marched and before I knew it, I was counting out my pennies: some rolling tobacco for Uncle William, a bottle of whisky, Charlie's favourite toffees and a bag of humbugs. When I finally forced them out of the door, my pocket was all but empty—no pleasant clinking of coins, just a sad feeling of loss.

'Cheer up, Geordie,' Jonno smiled. 'We may as well enjoy the spoils, boy.' He unscrewed the whisky bottle and took a long drink. 'Ahh...there now, boy, I feels a wonderful glow in me stomach and a tingling in me privates, now what could be better than that? Here now, have a drink.'

'I thought ye said it was for Uncle Will?'

'Ah, well,' he nodded. 'I can see ye need it more than himself, so take a long drink of the amber nectar while I roll meself a fag.'

'Hurry on Geordie, I'm next,' said Charlie.

So with Jonno tipping the bottle, I took my first non-medicinal drink. I'm not sure what happened after the bottle had come around for the third time, and I didn't really care.

'Roll me a fag then, Jonno,' says I. 'I may as well try one, if I'm to sample all of the devil's bad habits in one day.'

We sat smoking and drinking and getting even more reckless. The toffees stuffed into Charlie's pocket and the humbugs in mine were now of minor importance.

'Listen,' says Jonno, 'I know where we can find a girl who'll take her knickers off for a penny. What money can buy ye, eh Geordie? You'll have sampled every forbidden fruit known ti man, all in one day. And ye'll thank me for making a man of ye.'

'Oh yes,' says Charlie. 'I've seen ye with her, that's 'Maggie Crook a penny-a-look.' She goes to my school.'

By this time I was drunk and game for anything, my chromosomes were doing the highland fling and no reason could find its way into my befuddled brain. I was his and without any will of my own, my last penny was about to be spent.

We staggered down to the far end of the harbour where all the riffraff would hang out. I, embarrassed to be so excited about the wickedness at hand, could hardly sit still. We'd been left Charley and me, to sit on the harbour wall and wait while Jonno went to look for Maggie Crook.

We finished the last of the bottle between us, occasionally casting quick looks over our shoulder for the sinful Maggie. The movement of the water was having an upsetting effect on my stomach, the waves lapping against the timber walkway set my head spinning and my stomach to retching. I emptied the contents all down my front. Charlie was heaving next to me and a right pair we must have looked to Jonno as he rounded the corner of the alley and beckoned for us to come. We staggered after him around the corner of the alley, out of sight of prying eyes—and there she stood.

I recognised her face from school, though I'd never had the courage to speak to her and now she was standing here before me, full of confidence in the half light of the alley. She looked older and more beautiful than I remembered and was clearly in control of the situation. I, on the other hand, was in no fit state to appreciate the show we were about to see, so I allowed Jonno to hand over my penny.

'I never perform for minors,' she said theatrically, pointing at Charlie. 'Not unless you pay another halfpenny.' It seemed even her strict rules had their price. Jonno shook his head and led Charlie back to the mouth of the alley.

'Stay here and wait and I'll roll you a fag.' Charlie nodded, he was more annoyed that his attendance was only considered to be worth a halfpenny, but he sat down and was soon snoring.

I can't honestly say that I remember much of what was said, so mesmerised was I with the vision of the naked loveliness that stood before me, but of one thing I was certain: it was the best penny I had ever spent and I fell under Maggie Crook's spell that night in the alley during her show. She was able to generate such a feeling of overwhelming excitement that if I'd had my tin, she could have had it all. I'd never experienced anything like this before and it filled me with wonder.

'Next time, if ye bring tuppence,' she whispered, in her little girlish voice, 'I'll let you do it.'

I nodded dumbly with no real idea of what she meant, but quite sure I'd be back with tuppence.

We started home, staggering and singing and falling into the heather.

'Well, Geordie?' says Jonno. 'How does it feel to be a sinner then, boy?'

I couldn't tell him how I felt. I couldn't put words to it, plus I was quite sure he wouldn't understand the heavenly feeling that was swimming around in my mind.

I'd confused that little bit of wickedness with love, and I'd never view another girl in the same way again.

'I hope yer tin'll be safe, boy. Ye never know when we might hanker for another night on the town. We'd best check that it's safe when we get ye home. We'll help won't we Charlie?'

Charlie nodded, but the shaking of his head started him throwing up again. Something, some instinct, warned me that something wasn't quite right. In times of danger, drunkards have been known to sober up on the spot. Nothing could be more dangerous to me than to let Jonno loose with my tin, it was this very thought that shook my brain awake.

'Ye can leave me here now. I can cross the field on me own and thanks for coming.'

'Are ye sure now Geordie?' Jonno said, unable to keep the disappointment from his voice.

'We'll see ye across the field, won't we, Charlie?'

Charlie just smiled stupidly.

'Take him home now,' I insisted. 'I'm fine.'

I was making a good enough job of convincing Jonno that I was sober for him to give it up. They left me there and staggered off. I waved them out of sight and wove my way unsteadily across the field to the barn. Halfway across I had the feeling I was being stalked by Jezebel with a sore tit. I never found out if she was just a figment of my drunken imagination, but I ran the rest of the way, leaping the fence and rolling into the barn.

I awoke next morning with the cockerel crowing in my ear and with a drumming just above my eyes. I had the mother and father of hangovers and to move too quickly was to feel a bolt of lightning explode in my head. The full realisation of last night's events came crowding back. My first thought would have been my tin, if it hadn't been pushed aside by the picture of the naked Maggie in all her glory. I smiled at the thought, even though my head was on fire and I lay back so as not to disturb the picture and to replay over and over my own Penny Show.

My tin edged its way back into my thoughts and the realisation of its importance came back to me—without my tin, there would be no more Maggie. I leaped up in spite of the pain and went to the foot of the post near the wall, where I had excavated a hole, covered it with a sheet of tin and sprinkled hay over it. It lay undisturbed, at least that I could see. As I lifted the sheet and peered into the hole, my heart missed a beat. It was empty. My tin, my fortune, was gone.

'Geordie,' Angus shouted. 'Where are ye, boy? There's work to be done.'

I staggered out into the pale dawn light, screwing up my eyes to focus on Angus having his morning scrub.

'I can see from here ye've been on the drink boy, ye look an awful bloody mess. I canny pay full wages for a half-fit worker, so I hope ye dinny expect it.'

I shook my head despite the pain. I was in no mood for arguing the toss this morning.

'Maybe ye'll feel better after breakfast,' he said.

But the very thought of it had me retching.

Angus skipped inside huffing and puffing leaving an icy trail after him, while I stuck my head under the cold tap. The freezing water hit me like a slap in the face and it took the woolly feeling from my head. The importance of my missing tin came flooding back and I started back towards the barn.

'Where are ye off ti, Geordie? We've a mountain of work ti do, so ye'd better get started or I'll have to lift a little bit more of yer earnings.'

I made a quick about-turn, I wasn't going to give him the chance to snatch any more of my hard-earned pennies and I was quite sure he would work me longer and harder to make up for my lateness.

I was dead beat when we finally got back to the yard, and my eyes were drooping while I chewed on the gravy-soaked bread. No sympathy came my way from these two Presbyterian bigots. They thought it a disgrace to drink on a Sunday and Aggie suggested that I should pay penance by tidying the church garden in my own time. I dare not tell her what I had planned for Sunday afternoon down at the harbour or she'd have had a blue fit and Angus would have found a way to confiscate more of my wages. Any future meetings with Maggie, I decided, would have to be kept a very closely guarded secret.

My head banged on the table and woke me from my doze, with my mouth still full, I began to chew again. When my eyes finally opened, I saw that the dishes had all been cleared and I had been left alone. I lurched up and staggered over to the barn as I had the previous evening, but this time it was through sheer exhaustion. Tired as I was, I was determined to turn the barn upside down if necessary to find my tin. I looked again at the hole beneath the post and went over my movements of the previous night, wondering if I had replaced it there and it had been stolen. Would a thief carefully replace the sheet and hay? I doubted it. That meant I had stuffed it somewhere else, but, for the life of me, I had no idea where.

I scrabbled around for half an hour, cursing everyone who'd had the slightest opportunity to lift my tin, when I came upon it quite by accident. I had crashed down in the hay with exhaustion and landed on something hard. I'd stuffed it away from the prying eyes of my brothers, not having time to replace it in its rightful place. I pulled it to me gratefully and fell into a dreamless sleep.

By the end of the week, having worked like a Trojan, making or mending after work, I had clawed back all my losses. I had thought of nothing but Maggie, and each time I did, I came out in a sweat just remembering her escapades.

Sunday morning dragged by, but, with the chores done, I scrubbed up smartening myself as best I could and sat guiltily through the afternoon church service. I was sure that the fiery sermon about Sodom and Gomorra was somehow being aimed at me. I could feel Pastor McLean's eyes drawing my secrets from me, so that the whole congregation could read the guilt in my face. I was mightily relieved to leave, though I trembled when I shook his hand, with him blessing me for the hard work and faithfulness to Jesus and praising me for being such a help to Angus and my family. I wondered what he'd think if he knew what pictures were running through my mind at that very moment.

I presented myself for lunch trying hard to ignore the enquiring eyes from the other side of the table.

'I hope there'll be no repeat of last Sunday, Geordie McPhee,' Angus said.

He'd left out the threat, but it was there in his eyes.

'I'll have no drunken tinkers in my barn,' Aggie snapped. 'If ye get drunk, ye can sleep it off with the pigs.'

I managed to put on a serene look and shook my head in all the right places.

'Hmm,' she sniffed, as she left for the kitchen.

Angus still had something to say, I could see that and before I could slip away he stopped me in my tracks.

'It'll be a lassie, I'd be guessing, the way ye've slicked yer hair. A word for the better Geordie, be careful, they're more dangerous than the drink but put them both together and...' He let it drift, seeing quite clearly that I took his meaning. 'And remember yer Bible, remember Samson.'

The hair on the back of my neck stood out like a porcupine. I couldn't trust myself to speak. He'd see the lie, so I slid out the door and away. How had Angus guessed so easily? Was I so transparent? I hurried down the coast road, almost falling headlong several times in my haste to sin. I hadn't thought how I'd find her, or what I'd say if I did, but then good sense didn't stand a chance. I felt the coins, rattling in my pocket as I reached the place where the stain of our sickness still showed from our previous visit. I sat on the wall where Charlie and I had sat and looked in the water at my reflection.

What would my mother think of me, paying good money to sin? I coloured at the thought of her finding out, but the risk made it all the more exciting.

I dragged my eyes away and sat with the blood pounding in my temples in anticipation, nothing short of a bolt of lightning could stop me now. I calmed myself by taking deep breaths as Dada did when tickling trout and forced myself to abandon my thoughts and concentrate on the present. It was early yet, and some of the traders were still packing their barrows. My eyes were drawn to the mouth of the alley, I stared fixedly at it, willing her to come and frightened that she would. Perhaps I should have brought some rolling tobacco, I thought, to calm my nerves and to make me look a bit more grown up. I still had time to get to McReedie's if I ran.

I took off like a startled rabbit, down the harbour, casting backward looks in case she should arrive while I was away. Then quickly into the sweetie shop and out with the tobacco, papers and some matches. I was surprised at the price, they left me with only one penny and three farthings, but I had to have all three or none at all and my nerves were really jumping. Maybe Maggie would let me bring her the farthing another day.

I hurried back and rolled a sad-looking fag. I lit up and the empty paper flared burning my lip for my trouble—the bacci had fallen out as I'd bent to light it. I was a mess, my hands were shaking with my efforts to roll another tight tube.

'Give it here, Geordie,' a voice said.

I knew it was her. I had memorised that voice. I looked up into her big brown eyes and a knowing smile passed across her face. God, she was more beautiful than I remembered and like a servant, I passed the gubbins to her. She expertly rolled one for me and then one for herself, lighting them both, her face close to mine.

'Got yer tuppence then, Geordie boy?' she asked tartly.

'Well almost,' I said.

'Almost doesn't buy you very much, Geordie.'

'I'm a farthing short, but I'll bring it when I finish work tomorrow.'

'Perhaps we should wait for your treat until tomorrow then. You wouldn't want to short change me.'

I was crestfallen. I could die tonight and never keep that appointment.

'I could do you a little dance for a penny and I'll let you stroke me for another three halfpence, how's that?'

I nodded like an obedient slave and she led me to the alley. The money changed hands and the dance began. I was beside myself, especially as it was for me alone. Maggie reached for my hand and I gave it to her. She placed it on her breast and I thought I had never felt such a thrill run through me.

'Ye can stroke me if ye like, Geordie. I won't break,' she whispered.

I'd felt the softness of ferrets and young rabbits, with the life coursing through them, but nothing that could compare to my brown-eyed Maggie. The feel of her soft downy skin was like the softest kind of velvet. I stroked her like a cat until I felt my blood boil, then, like a slap in the face or being dowsed with cold water, she said, 'I have to go now, Geordie, but ye come and see me again with tuppence and we'll have fun.'

I ran all the way up the coast road, reliving my first encounter with the angels and wondering what could be better in this whole world than what I had just encountered. I was thirteen years old and very nearly a man this night. I was quite sure that Maggie must love me, as I loved her, to allow me such pleasure.

I was bright and happy next morning when I came in for breakfast and I cared not at all that Angus and Aggie were giving me knowing looks.

'What were ye up ti, if ye don't mind the asking?' Angus said between mouthfuls of porridge.

'Nothing,' says I, 'nothing very exciting that is, just the normal talking and joking and swapping stories with me brothers.'

It sounded very unconvincing and clearly it didn't satisfy their curiosity.

'Only,' says he, 'yer brothers came looking for ye. I said ye was in bed and I sent them away with a flea in their ear.'

A silence descended over the room as I was caught out in my first lie.

'Aye, they found me down at the harbour later. Jonno told me he'd asked ye about me.'

'Oh no,' Geordie, 'it was the little curly one who came, Charlie.'

I was getting deeper and deeper in the mire and decided not to prolong the conversation.

'Better get milking Jezebel, she gets cranky if she has to wait' and with that I slipped out of the kitchen with a sigh of relief. Jezebel was more relaxed than usual. I seemed now to have a gentler touch that she liked and as I coaxed her milk from her, my mind strayed back to the alley. I must away to see my mother this Sunday, I thought, and take her a present. Maggie would have to bide her time, but even as I said it I knew this decision was not cast in stone and the draw of the sinful Maggie would be too great. I would just have to see her one day after work, perhaps even tomorrow.

Once decided, tomorrow could come none too soon for me. I was bewitched and caught in the current of a powerful urge to learn more of the secrets of love.

I slept fitfully that night. The dark was full of imaginings but I managed to get through the day and now I was ready to go. I'd robbed my tin again—this time I took three pence to be sure. If tuppence gave you the ultimate pleasure, then heaven knows what three pence might do. My tool savings were now going down at a faster rate than I could put them back and just the thought of it rankled, but I knew that I would gladly pay twice that much had Maggie asked.

Still, the ultimate prize, as she called it, was getting expensive and one part of me hoped it would prove disappointing so that I could return to my steady ways and not have my mind filled morning, noon and night with this all-powerful desire.

The thrill that Maggie had introduced into my life was now in my blood and I was forced to accept that I would never willingly be without it.

I was about to leave when Jonno arrived.

'Geordie, are ye going somewhere, boy?'

'No,' says I.

'What are ye all scrubbed up for then?'

'Aye well, I was going to see mother, but it's a bit late. I think I might just take a walk around the farm.'

I cursed him under my breath for the scallywag that he was. Jonno never missed an opportunity, he was after sharing my money, I knew that for a fact.

'I just called in to see if ye wanted some more of the same,' he smiled. 'I left Charlie at home. He's a bit young for the lassies yet and he canny keep his tongue from wagging. It was all around the school that we had a viewing of the delectable Maggie.'

'Oh, that,' I said, my heart thumping. 'I was drunk and the truth to tell, I can hardly remember a thing except that me tin was sixpence short.'

'Ye mean ye canny remember the sight of ye first naked girl? Ye never stopped talking about it all the way home. Well, we could always have a drink instead,' he suggested.

'I canny afford it after the last time. I have to save my money for a set of tools.'

'Well then, lend me a penny for some rolling tobacco and I'll leave ye be.' I pulled a penny from me pocket and it hurt to give it, as I knew right well that I would never see it back, but I had to get rid of him and as soon as possible. I needn't have worried he disappeared as soon as the money touched his hand.

After five minutes, I followed at a run and I hoped nothing more would go wrong and she would materialise as she had only the day before yesterday.

I sat on the harbour wall in the same place as I had previously and waited stupefied with anticipation. A minute seemed like an hour, the time passed so slowly that I began to wonder if my worst fears might be realised and God forbid, she wouldn't turn up. I remembered that my elaborate plan had not been shared with her and the arrangement to meet on this day was concocted only at the last minute in my thoughts. I would have to go look for her as Jonno had. I walked casually over to the mouth of the alley and peeked in. It was empty. Should I call her name? What if someone else came and they recognised me, and worse still guessed why I was there?

I hovered on the edge of the alley, deciding whether to stay, go look, or run home. If I stayed here, she still might find me, but if I ran home, I faced days of disappointment. I went to look for her, deciding it was better to do something than nothing. I crept up the alley and as I turned the corner, I heard a giggle coming from the far end. It was her voice, of that I was sure. I blundered toward it and almost ran into Jonno.

'Geordie, what are ye doing here? Come sit, you're just in time for the show.'

'I thought ye wanted rolling tobacco,' I said dumbfounded.

'Ah, well yer see,' said Jonno with a smile, 'smoking is bad for yer chest, whereas Maggie is good for your other bits, so I chose Maggie.'

'Will you boys pay attention? I'm getting cold and you're halfway through your penny.'

My eyes stared unblinking as she went though her routine and as my temperature began to rise, so did my manhood. I was embarrassed and excited all at the same time. Not so Jonno, who kept muttering all the way through. As she finished, he complained that he'd seen this same routine many times before and she would have to come up with some new material if she wanted to keep his custom.

'What di ye expect for a penny, Jonno McPhee?'

'Well, ye'll be getting no more pennies from us Maggie Crook. Isn't that right, Geordie?'

I just raised my eyebrows in a non-committal way, so as not to hurt her feelings.

'I should have chosen me tobacco instead,' he complained. 'I think I'm due a refund.'

Jonno started to rise, dragging me with him and as he turned to Maggie, I thrust a penny into his hand and said he should go smoke himself to death if he so wished, but I'd stay here.

'Thanks, Geordie boy, it's only a loan though, ye understand.' He shuffled off up the alley, leaving me and the now fully-dressed Maggie alone. She was sniffling at the insult that he had poured on her only asset and the far-reaching effect it might have on her earning power if he should repeat his dissatisfaction to the local boys.

'Geordie, you liked the penny thrill, didn't ye?' she asked without much confidence. I nodded to save her tears and though I didn't tell her, the third time of seeing didn't quite match the first. She could see I was there for more and whispered in my ear that if I had tuppence she'd put the smile back on my face.

'I had to give Jonno his penny back to get rid of him, but I still have tuppence.'

I held the two pennies out in the palm of my hand and her eyes lit up, she whisked the coins from my hand in a flash and her dress came off just as fast. I lost my soul to the devil in the alley and I became a man with the help of fourteen-year-old Maggie Crook.

I slept fitfully that night, recounting snatches of the beautiful Maggie, only disturbed by the sound of Jezebel mewing in the background. Some unfamiliar sounds, not to my mind belonging to the farm, nudged me awake. I lay in the dark barn, my mind filling with imaginings. I concentrated my ears on the sound that seemed out of place. I was sure as I wandered outside into the yard that it must be my own imagination playing tricks on me and I almost turned back. The sound I'd been listening for came floating to me on the night air, secretive, like a whisper. Peering hard through a black sky pierced only by the stars shimmering above and the pale light from the crescent of the moon, I crept toward the cowsheds.

The silence around the farm was often absolute and on a still night I could hear the thrashing of a cow's tail from my barn, so I slipped my boots off and glided silently forward. Jezebel was being led quietly from her stall, something wrapped around her hooves to lessen the sound. Two figures were all I could see but instinct told me that they were tinkers, 'on the rob', and Jezebel was their target. What to do? Should I let well alone, and risk losing Angus's his best milk cow, or tackle them myself. What would Dada do, I knew of course that he would be a match for them, he was well known for his strength, but I was a boy trying to be a man. They were almost out as I stepped into the doorway blocking their exit. They were caught, surprised, and unsure of how many we were.

'Ye canny take Angus's milk cow,' I said firmly, trying to keep the shake from my voice, 'he has the protection of the McPhees.' It was a moment of inspiration, and my best chance of success. I could see them hesitate. My Dada's family's reputation was well known in tinker circles around Wick.

'Ye'd best leave before I raise Angus and his dogs.'

'Geordie, is that you?' said a voice I recognised as belonging to Jonno. 'It's me and Uncle Will. Let us be boy, before anyone else wakes.'

'Uncle Will ye canny rob Angus, he has our word ti let him be, he'll finish me if he thinks it's tinkers and Dada will be angry and make ye take it back, so ye'd best just leave and no more said.'

'Ah the old skinflint can afford one milk cow, Geordie, and she'd be right handy on the Isles.'

'Angus has been good ti me and I won't see him robbed, so if ye take her, Dada will know it from me.'

'Come Jonno, I wouldn't want ti upset yer Dada, he's stubbornly honest that man. We'll find some skinflint farmer who's more deserving of our attention. No hard feelings Geordie, but it's the law of survival boy, so don't hold it against us.'

They left, and I crept back to bed not quite sure of whose side I should've been on, where my allegiance should lie and with a feeling that I'd let my family down. This was to be the beginning of my denial, although I didn't know it then.

I managed to get through the day but Angus could see something was wrong and badgered me to share my problem. I told him it was nothing, but he was shrewd enough to know that I was keeping something back, he shrugged, and let it go. It wasn't until next tea time that he spoke of some thieving in the area and how lucky he had been to escape scot free. He gave me a look that said he knew that I had had something to do with his escape, though he couldn't know what.

I awoke feeling good, Maggie had sent me home feeling like a man and my intervention that saved Jezebel made the feeling complete. I was Maggie's slave for a time, sneaking back and forth at her every whim. I was now obliged to meet her in the picture show at the village hall on Saturday nights, to show that I was serious. It didn't stop her raising the price of my treat to three pence. She said it was on account of her having grown in all the right places. Now there was more of her to see and touch, it seemed only fair she should raise the price. That part of the proceedings was kept firmly on a business footing.

I gradually began to cool off and bring a little order to my life, starting once again to think about the future. I still saw Maggie often after that night to quench my desire, but what had once been an all-consuming love had now turned into a cheap thrill, a hurried act of passion to end a Saturday night. The weight of my tin would remind me, however, that the term 'cheap thrill' wasn't entirely accurate. I felt new priorities come to the front and I worked hard for my tools. I asked Angus to negotiate for me, for a consideration of course and with his help I managed finally to purchase a fine set of carpentry tools from the widow of a local tradesman and I used them at every opportunity.

I was back to normal now and took the time to visit my mother once a week, fulfilling my promise to make her some rockers for her nursing chair, which became her pride and joy. I'd take Jeannie and Hughie to the sweetie shop and occasionally to the picture show in the lean-to at the back of the Highlander pub.

Mr McNab, the projectionist, would slip out the rear door as soon as the film started and the lights went down, into the adjoining bar where he quickly spent the day's takings. He refused to come back when the film jammed, at least until he had no more money, by which time he was too drunk to stand. The booing he received was loud and long, but it was water off a duck's back. During a brief lull, he'd say that due to technical problems and circumstances beyond his control, he was unable to finish the film show and would return to the bar.

He was only too happy to give me instructions in the workings of the projector, so I would pay to get in and work the projector while he promptly got drunk and fell asleep. I refused to stand in on a Saturday night when Maggie was with me. The film on those occasions was of no importance and I wouldn't dare leave her out there alone in the dark or I would be sure to be paying for someone else's cheap thrill. Of course, I knew she had other boys, and at first it hurt my pride, but now my feelings were different. I hadn't the time or patience to court one of the other local girls—that would mean going through the difficult process of being accepted by parents, who knew I was a tinker boy, and behaving with propriety, spending my hard-earned money without any reward or treat. No, Maggie would do for me.

Things jogged along. I started to do the odd carpentry job on a Sunday in the town and I was becoming well known for my cheapness. Things would have continued happily if Maggie hadn't dropped her bombshell. It was a Saturday night and we had arranged to see the latest movie. I met her on the harbour and I could tell from a distance that something was wrong. When I reached her, I could see she'd been crying.

'What is it, Maggs?' I said. 'You look upset.'

'Oh, Geordie, I've a bun in the oven,' she moaned.

I must have looked puzzled because she frowned.

'I'm up the duff,' she said, with an urgency that made me look up.

Still it hadn't penetrated but I began to feel wary.

'I'm having a fucking baby, ye dozy tinker,' she blasted in my ear and pointed at her stomach.

I stood rooted to the spot. What had I done? What should I do? I was in a daze.

'W...W...What? Why? How?' was all I could get out. I felt the trap closing and I couldn't get out of the way. I wouldn't be the first teenage father. I'd seen many at the tinker gatherings, and many child mothers a lot younger than Maggie. But I had plans and they didn't include a wife and child. She could see my frightened look and wrinkled her nose.

'It may not be yours, if that's what yer thinking. I'm not right sure yet whose it is. I don't think you're quite up to the mark yet, boy. I'm upset 'cause me earning power will soon be zero and I'll get the mother and father of a thrashing off me dad and he'll kick me out for sure, Geordie.'

I took this good news on the chin, while I was still reeling from the last blow, and felt totally out of my depth. That's when I made my next fatal error. So grateful was I that I'd been pardoned on the scaffold on the eve of my hanging, so to speak, that I offered her my tin and all its contents. She kissed me long and hard and tore at her clothing, but I was in no mood for passion.

'I'll get my tin then,' I said 'and ye'd better get off home.'

But if I thought I could shake myself free, she had another thought coming up on the rails. She clung to me like a second skin as we stormed up the coast road, she hanging on to my arm as if I'd fly off given the slightest chance. We arrived at the barn and crept in. There was no point in care now, my year's work, my savings would be gone, so I pulled it from its hiding place and handed it to her before she could change her mind and lay the blame on me.

Maggie couldn't keep the smile from her face.

'How about a special treat ye'll never forget, ti say thank you?'

My mind boggled to think of what she could possibly do that would be worth twenty shillings and four pence. But I was desperate to see her go, so I stood awkwardly and wished her all the best and watched as she took my hard-earned money and vanished. They say a fool and his money are soon parted, and I was the living proof of the truth of that little piece of wisdom.

I was to steer clear of the harbour now that my fingers had been badly burned and I'd try to put this last incident behind me. It was to be our secret. I threw myself into the work to ease my conscience and the sight of my efforts put a permanent smile on Angus's face. I hadn't left the farm for weeks now, even though I'd been pestered relentlessly by Jonno and Charlie to come and have some fun, paid for by me, of course. I'd had to tell them that my money had been stolen and I was as broke as the pair of them.

'No Maggie then,' Jonno said.

'No,' I shook my head, to give it finality 'no anything.'

I'd had messages from my mother asking if all was well and should she send Dada to fetch me home. I sent Charlie to say that I was working very hard and would come as soon as the work eased off. Charlie stopped coming after a while, and with Jonno off to the Western Isles with our uncle, I was left in peace to reflect on my foolishness. Still, my kitty was starting to accumulate again and that made me feel better. Eventually, I plucked up the courage to venture into town to see my mother and ran headlong into the gossip that was rife concerning Maggie Crook and the sudden thickening of her usually neat waist. She had now been banned from school, as rumours spread that she was pregnant, she was regarded as a bad example to the other girls and a temptation to all the boys. She was whisked away like a bad smell, excluded and shunned by the church, which righteously condemned her as a harlot. She would have been confined to the workhouse for her wickedness, if they'd had their way. Speculation was growing about who the father might be, and interrogations of the local boys as to who she'd been seeing bore no fruit. Maggie was questioned about who the father could be but she refused to name anyone, mainly because she didn't know.

She'd been seen hanging around down by the harbour, so they reasoned it could have been any one of the riffraff that frequented the bars. Her father, in a fit of anger at losing her earnings, had promised to give a thrashing to within an inch of his life to the perpetrator of the crime against his little girl. I listened to this with mounting fear. I knew it was only a matter of time before my name joined the list of boys seen on the same harbour wall, and being a tinker boy would not help my case. Maggie had said the baby may not be mine but that wouldn't carry much weight around here, and under pressure she may well change her mind. With Jonno out of the way, I was left to worry alone.

What should I do? Who could I talk to? I answered my own question—Dada. He was my only salvation and though I dreaded facing him, I knew he would stand by me. I made my way home on legs of jelly and was glad to see that my mother was out with the children and Dada was fashioning a pot for the weekday market.

'Geordie boy, how are ye?' he said with a smile attached.

'Fine, Dada,' I replied rather stupidly. I mean, nothing could have been further from the truth. Where was my confession going to go from here? I needn't have worried, his sharp eyes could always read me like a book and that must have been an easy task this day. I caught sight of myself in the reflection from a pan hanging behind him and I hardly recognised myself.

'Sit yourself down son,' he said, patting the box next to him.

He'd never called me son before this indeed was a day of firsts. I bent my head and the shame came out of me in a torrent of tears.

'What have ye done that's so terrible, Geordie?' he asked in his quiet voice.

'I did it with Maggie Crook and now she's having a bain. They'll think it's mine.'

'Are ye the father, does she say?'

'She doesn't know, Dada, but that won't stop them townies, they'll blame me 'cause I'm a tinker boy.'

'Steady as ye go, boy. That isn't so terrible, curiosity being part of growing up as it is, and pleasure-seeking being part of all of us. It's as much my fault as yours. I should have learned ye a bit more about the natural things of life. Di ye love this wee girl, Geordie?'

'I had a passion, Dada, and I couldn't contain it.'

He hugged me to him and I felt safe in his care. 'Dada,' I whispered, 'sooner or later they'll find me.'

'Aye, maybe the self-righteous mob will, but ye're safe here boy, for now. Geordie, me advice to yer is plain. I said ye would have to leave some day for yer own sake, and never look back. I think that time has come. They're building a great road south of Thurso and it's going all the way ti England. I sold some pots to the cook and he told me they were looking for a man to look after the Irish navvies, who're doing the digging. So if ye've a mind to go, gather yer tools, Geordie, and I'll take ye there. They leave on Friday early.'

I was apprehensive, scared, but I had no choice. If I stayed, someone was sure to tell that I'd been seeing Maggie, and heaven knows what they'd demand from me. At best I'd be marrying her and the life would be strangled out of me. I'd be landed with a wife and a child that could have been fathered by any one of a dozen boys, even Jonno. From what I'd been hearing, Maggie hadn't been very choosy, but I still felt bad. Maggie was my first love and I'd never forget her.

My Dada rode me home in the wagon and spoke softly to me.

'Geordie,' he said, 'when ye were born, yer mother made a promise to God that life for ye'd be different, and God in his own way, has answered her. Ye have yer chance now to start yer life again. When ye leave Wick, Geordie, go without a backward glance and only look forward. You're young and ye have a sensitive nature, but ye have tinker iron in ye, so if they call ye jock and ask ye what ye wear under yer kilt, stand yer ground and be proud of yer heritage."

He talked of his time in the Great War when he thought never to see his family or homeland again. He'd fought shoulder to shoulder with men of all types and nationalities, and he'd learned to put his trust in them.

'At first I felt like a fish out of water but I survived and so will ye.'

It was the last piece of good advice my Dada was ever to give me. What worried me now was what I'd say to my mother, and if I had the courage to walk away from my life and all the people in it. I spent a restless week mulling over my past, such as it was. I'd come from a tinker boy living off the land to a farm labourer with carpentry skills. Angus would miss me and I wrestled with whether I should tell him and what he'd do if I did. In the end I settled for leaving him a note, thanking him for teaching me the carpentry skills and putting a good word in for Charlie. He could do worse than follow the example of Angus, he would certainly learn thrift to curb his wasteful ways if nothing else.

I woke early on Friday morning and it was still dark as I crept out of the barn and made my way across the field to the road. As I climbed the wooden rails, I was butted from behind, and the boy inside my skin must have jumped high enough to clear it, while the rest of me was frozen on the first rung. I hadn't heard Jezebel as she plodded up behind me and nudged me with her nose. I sat on the fence shaking, my nerves hanging by a thread. I stroked her muzzle and she lowed softly. We'd become great friends after a thorny start, and the unconditional love of the farm animals would always be special to me, a mutual trust that I hadn't found in the human form, apart from my own family. The tears that sprung from me when saying goodbye to Jezebel were as much me saying goodbye to the last fourteen years of my life.

As I sat waiting for Dada, holding back the feeling of panic, I forced myself to plan for the future. I would call myself George as I had been christened. It would sound more English than Geordie. I would be George McPhee, a carpenter from Wick, and that would be all I would volunteer. There would be no tinker stories to tell future friends. I'd have to draw a curtain over my family background and start again. With that decided, I was ready to face the future. My father came, as he'd promised he would, with my whole family, to see me off and wish me well. What he'd told my mother, I'll never know, but I suspect she'd have had the truth out of him. Though the desperation showed in her eyes, she never shed a tear in my presence.

Dada introduced me to Liam O'Donahue, the ganger, a huge Irishman with a soft lilting brogue and startling blue eyes. He also had the red hair of a tinker, and if I wasn't mistaken, he would have the fiery to go with it. He told me that I would have to make and mend the living quarters, as his lads tended to get a bit frisky when they'd had a little drink, which he explained was most nights. I was to accompany him to the pubs in the cart and round them up and bed them down.

As this generally ended in a free-for-all, I'd have to mend, as best I could, any damage to the wooden shed or its contents. This didn't seem too difficult a task to me as it was what I'd been doing for Angus when the animals lashed out.

I'd be paid one shilling per week from every perpetrator who caused damage. This was to be deducted from their wages and passed on to me by Liam, to add to a basic fifteen shillings per week from the company. I could only nod at the fortune I was about to make, and pray, God forgive me, for a quarrelsome journey.

I said a tearful goodbye to my family and promised to write and send back some money to help them along. Jonno said to send word when I reached London. He'd heard somewhere that the streets were paved with gold, and if they were, he'd come running. Charlie added that I should keep a penknife under my pillow at night, as it was well known that the English were very sneaky and would rob ye blind. Jeannie and Hughie just cried, more because there would be no more sweeties and cinema on a Saturday night. I gave them a penny each and that seemed to do the trick. My mother and father just looked sad. I was sailing for foreign parts and they felt partly to blame.

§

Chapter Five

Geordie's Escape

We pulled out that afternoon, me with a heavy heart accompanied by a sense of excitement, on to a great expanse of tarmacadam running like a black river as far as the eye could see and as smooth as Maggie Crook's creamy skin. I shook my head and banished that thought from my mind—thinking like that had got me into my present position. I'd made up my mind that though women could cast a wonderful spell, they also carried a terrible sharp sting in their tail.

We'd reached the furthest point of the road and it seemed to peter out into wilderness. I learned later that after working from dawn to dusk all week, we would eventually catch up with the engineers plotting the course, and would have a day off in the nearest town. That's how fate had brought them to Wick.

The crew disembarked, and like a well-oiled machine, they began to dig and level the ground behind a clumsy bulldozer as it pushed its way through the litter of rocks and trees, following the guide pegs that stretched out before it.

I was a general gopher sent to fetch water caskets for the sweating men, and on occasions, to fetch Liam whenever a fight broke out over a shovel or a pick. I marvelled at Liam's 'persuader,' an Indian club called Dolly, which in his hands was a fearsome weapon. He'd bounce it on a few heads to restore order in record time, and then I'd be sent for the first aid to patch up the wounded. I liked looking after these big Irishmen, they worked like horses, swore like troopers and drunk beer faster than the barmaids could pour it, but they were honest and generous and they had taken a liking to their little Scottie mascot.

Come the first Friday of my employment I joined the queue for my wages and this proved to be a battle to put Angus McDonald to shame. Every man disputed the yardage that Liam had set. The yardage that was completed was divided by the workforce and multiplied by a price that was set in stone, and in this case, it had come out lower than expected. These big navvies had never seen the inside of a schoolhouse but they would know how far they'd come, give or take a yard, and guess how much they'd earned, just by experience. The arguing was getting heated, and hands were clenched into fists. Liam took a firm hold on Dolly as they all pushed forward to put in their pennyworth. This looked like developing into a war.

'Ye can't have what ye haven't earned me, boyo,' Liam said, and went through the calculation again slowly. He was wasting his time, for nobody understood the mathematics—except me, that is. I could see the yardage was being divided by everyone on site from the cook to the gopher. Half of us were not working to increase it, but still our wages came from the same pot. When I arrived Liam had told me that the company paid my basic wage and I was sure this applied to all the other non-producers. If so, someone was pocketing our shares.

I dare not say too much, I could have been wrong, but the gang knew they were being short-changed and they wouldn't settle. This had been brewing for some time, so I gathered from what was said, and they'd had enough. They agreed to meet in the local pub and decide what to do, and I was invited to join them. Beer stokes up the emotions and dulls the senses, and this combination doesn't help when trying to solve a problem. Something would have to be decided before they got too drunk. I should mind my business, I thought. I was still green and unsure which side I should be on.

I was getting paid, and with the crew getting angry, I could be in for a bonus, if they took it out on the shed, that is. Liam had been good to me, we worked together, so I couldn't accuse him of fiddling the figures or I might get a taste of Dolly and be sent on my way. For better or worse, Dada had taught me honesty, a rare commodity amongst the tinkers, and a ball and chain when dealing with the wily ones. He'd told me never to be afraid to stand up and be counted for what I believed. This code had only got my Dada into the trenches of France, gained him respect but not much else. In view of this and because I was my father's son, I resolved to see Liam. I'd tell him he'd been rumbled and give him the chance to put things right before another World War broke out.

I walked into the pub in time to hear John-Joe Feeley, a big curly-haired tinker, cursing the very ground Liam walked on, and suggesting we tar and feather him and hang him up by his goolies until he'd come clean about how the fiddle was being worked and by whom. A loud cheering followed this suggestion. It seemed that the case was closed and the sentence would be carried out at closing time. They were in no mood to waste precious drinking time, so I made my exit and headed quickly back to camp. I found Liam nursing a bottle of scotch and already three sheets to the wind.

'Welcome, my little Georgie,' he said, with a huge grin. 'Come and join meself in a glass of the finest whisky outside of dear old Dublin. Sit yourself down,' he said, pointing his glass at a wooden crate.

'Liam," I said, trying to compose myself, 'there's trouble brewing. The lads have rumbled a fiddle and they're after yer hide.'

'Fiddle! What fiddle?' he shouted, swaying as he tried to stand.

I was stranded on dangerous ground here. I didn't really know which way to tread. I moved on gingerly.

'They say the company should pay the wages of the non-producers and only the road layers should share the yardage. They're threatening to see the boss, after seeing ti ye first.'

I could see by his face that he was puzzled by my story, but it was plain enough that I had guessed right.

'Who's stirring the shit then, Georgie, tell me that? I'll bend Dolly across his head, so I will.'

I remained silent. It wouldn't do to take sides. I'd started out with the intention of averting a war, but if I were to do that, I would have to be crafty.

'Someone's been cheating ye, Liam, and they're looking to ye to set it right.'

'Ah,' he said, sobering by the minute. 'It'll be one of them English bastards getting rich on me lads' toil and be Jesus, when I find him, I'll twist his miserable neck.'

'Can I tell them that ye've sorted it for them and they'll get their full share come Friday?'

'You most certainly can, boyo,' he said, taking a long swig from the bottle. 'Those lads are like me own flesh and blood.' He said it without conviction or the usual smile, knowing full well that his days on the gravy train were over.

By the time I arrived back at the pub most were legless and incapable of doing any damage to anyone except themselves, but feelings were still running high and John-Joe was repeating the sentence of the kangaroo court to anyone who'd listen. I'd have to hurry or Liam would come to collect them with the cart and heaven knows what might happen then. I tried to make myself heard above the singing of Danny Boy but it was hopeless. They were dancing on shaky legs and making a fair mess of the bar.

'Hey there, Georgie, have a pint with me now, and don't say no. It's a pint for young Georgie if you please, me darling,' John-Joe slurred.

I was pulled into the drunken, dancing crowd that staggered from bar to door, clearing everything that got in the way. My pint arrived and I was pushed into the centre of the group, which was now chanting for me to down the pint in one. I had to try, but, by halfway it was running back out of my mouth, having filled my stomach and having nowhere else to go.

'I propose a toast!' I shouted raising my glass in desperation. 'To John-Joe Feeley.'

That stopped them in their tracks and they all began to slap John-Joe on the back, with him thanking them and nodding with an idiot's grin on his face.

'I'd be best pleased to know what it was I'd done, now Georgie,' he said.

The place went quiet. Drunk or not they were as keen as John-Joe to know.

'Liam's coming here tonight to tell ye all that he'll put yer wages right and he'll seek out the sneaky English bastard who's been cheating ye.'

A huge cheer went up and there was a headlong rush to the bar.

By the time Liam arrived, there wasn't a man standing.

It was a strength-sapping operation, dragging, carrying and lifting the semi-conscious and unconscious navvies into the cart, and at the end of three runs we had lost count and were too tired to care. Those we'd missed would sleep under the stars come rain, hail, or snow and we'd round them up in the morning. I said goodnight to Liam, and at our parting he smiled a wicked smile.

'Thanks, my little Georgie. Ye saved an awful lot o' bloodshed, so you did, and Liam O'Donahue never forgets a favour.'

He'd guessed, of course, that the settlement was my doing, and from that day on he swore to be my protector and I had good cause to bless him for it.

We slept in rows of wooden cradles in the one hut and it stunk to high heaven. All through the night one or other would stagger up, weave his way to the door, and if we were lucky, he'd open it and ye'd hear the loud splashing accompanied by a huge fart, which added new life to the stench that hung over us. By morning the door was hanging off and I found two of my gang spread-eagled on the ground outside.

Liam was ringing the breakfast bell, and just like magic, they rose from their unconscious stupor and filed down the road to the canteen.

This was yet another wooden hut I was responsible for and it was manned by a large Irish girl. Her name, I learned, was nutty Nancy O'Reardon—a title she came by, not because of the state of her mind, that was sharp enough…no, I was left to find out for myself the reason for such a name, and it didn't take long.

Halfway down the breakfast queue on my second week, there

was a commotion. As the queue moved on, I stumbled over Mickey-the-Creep who was stretched out on the floor with blood streaming from his nose. He'd failed to take notice of Nancy's reputation and was butted for his ignorance, he being stupid enough to let his hand stray to her fulsome figure without an invitation. Mickey seemed always to choose the wrong options, such was his nature. He was a tiny man, made to look smaller by the size of the navvies around him, with the sharp features of a weasel. He could be mistaken for a jockey, and the way he rode his luck, it was a good job he had John-Joe Feeley as his protector, though it hadn't saved him from Nancy.

'Tell that pint-sized little creep to keep his dirty hands to himself, John-Joe, or his nose won't be the only thing I'll break,' she said, moving her eyes slowly down below John-Joe's waist. John-Joe moved uncomfortably, nodded, and whispered an apology on Mickey's behalf.

Nancy was a handsome lass, not unlike my own aunt Elizabeth, and it was she who doled out bowls of thick porridge that coated your insides like cement and was well known for keeping out the cold. Nancy wasn't the only girl who rode with our happy group. There were two cooks, Eileen and Mary, for the engineers, and a laundry girl named Peggy. All would join us on a Saturday night at the local pubs. We weren't always welcome, though, and sometimes the locals would turn up in force and a battle would take place. The three girls would pitch in and could wreak havoc if they isolated some poor local man whose misplaced manners stopped him from weighing in.

'These little fracas's,' as Liam called them, were looked forward to eagerly by my gang, whose perfect night consisted of a skin full of beer, a good fight and then, for the lucky ones who were still sober, a night in the canteen shed with one of the girls. Liam considered all this was good for his lads, keeping them in good spirits. For me, I tried to keep out of trouble, but if I was getting a beating, Liam would come to my rescue, swinging Dolly.

§

Chapter Six

The Dirty Tinkers

This was how it went, hard work, hard drinking and new faces to love or fight. We ate up the miles through the highlands, skirting the lochs in the relatively flat terrain, but it was changing. In the distance I could see the vast pine forests set on limestone hills rising to meet a granite spine that seemed an impossible obstacle. I had no knowledge of how the engineers would drive the road through or round this seemingly impossible barrier and I was moved to ask Liam how you could overcome a mountain, on our ride to the pub.

'Well now, Georgie,' he said, showing me his two huge hands. 'What these can't shift, the dynamite will.'

This was the first mention of blasting that I'd heard.

'Sure, it's a bit risky, a tiny bit unpredictable in the wrong hands. We lost a few good men through carelessness last year, so you better stick close by me when it begins.'

Our workforce doubled and trebled in the following week as the word spread that the company was recruiting broad backs and strong arms to excavate a tunnel through the mountain that stood defiantly in our way. Gangs were appearing from all directions, tinkers most of them, from the Western Isles. They'd come in convoys with their families and camped in the fields beside the road. I had an uncomfortable feeling that when the drink started to flow, all hell could break loose. Dada had told me that he'd been hired to tunnel for the railway, but the place became a magnet for all the dirty tinkers and thieves in Scotland, so he took us back to Wick.

I'd already seen my gang eyeing up the opposition, and when Liam locked the pick handles away, I began to worry. My apprehension heightened when the pubs of Pittlochry proved to be too far to go, so it was the home-made poteen and the young tinker girls that the men headed for. They sat around the fire, telling tales of mythical proportions, each side trying to out-boast the other. The exaggerations grew wilder as the drink took hold and I prayed that neither side would challenge the authenticity of the teller. This, I knew, would signal the death-knell for what, up to now, had been an amiable, if untypically, friendly meeting. I knew the characteristics of both and could see the signs that would lead us down the path to confrontation.

It's an insignificant little disturbance that starts the pebble rolling, and it can quickly turn into an avalanche. My being in the position of having one foot in either camp sparked memories of Tam MacKay and his efforts to keep the peace for my family's sake, though how I could stop what seemed an inevitable clash defeated me. I hovered on the periphery, as the posturing began. Arm-wrestling seemed to be the solution, as a sporting test of strength, it was better than losing teeth, but the loss of face for either group was likely to light the fuse to a keg of dynamite.

The crowds were gathering as John-Joe Feeley shaped up with a challenge for the tinkers to send out their best man.

'I'll crush his hand and deck his knuckles in a second,' he said. John-Joe was a big man, tall with huge hands, and whilst the tinker men were broad, they were much shorter. They could find no one with the arm length to make a match with John-Joe, and he was claiming the contest.

'It's a walkover,' he slurred, and with the poteen loosening his tongue, he christened the tinkers a tribe of 'highland pygmies' and paraded himself around the fire. A deadly quiet descended, disturbed only by the crackle of the burning logs.

'I have a suggestion to make,' I said. All eyes turned to me. This was the second time I'd tried to smooth the troubled waters, and I cursed myself for my impetuous tongue. My own prowess at arm-wrestling I had inherited from my father, so I placed myself as the gang's representative, and had no end of tinker lads willing to take me on. If I should win either group could claim me as their own and no face would be lost. And if I lost, then they would both disown me. Either way they escaped the humiliation of defeat.

I remembered the evenings with Dada, Jonno on one arm and me on the other, being taught how to gain an advantage in the delicate art of table wrestling. I always had strong arms and I prayed they wouldn't let me down. I knew these tinkers by reputation, and my Dada would have none of them. He said they were the dirty tinkers who'd slit yer throat for a shilling. I had the horrible feeling that if things went wrong, I could be the cause of the bloodshed, rather than saving us all from it. With this in mind, I was tempted to extricate myself before they came up with a suitable opponent. Unfortunately they'd found a lad about my age and height and I soon learned that his name was Bully from the shouts of encouragement he was receiving.

He was named after a particularly fierce bull that had dispatched his father only days after his birth, so I was told later, and I was thankful that it wasn't known to me before the battle began. They had regained the advantage in weight and I began to sweat. The two of us squared up. The betting was rife and the advice was constant. John-Joe was massaging my arms to bring life to my muscles.

'A word of advice now, Geordie,' he said.

I looked him in the eye, expecting a secret formula that might give me an advantage over this confident-looking tinker boy.

'Don't lose,' he said, as he popped a wooden peg into my mouth. 'Bite on it, boy, like yer mother did when ye was birthed.'

A table appeared with two logs to sit on. Our wrists were bound and our elbows placed together in the centre of the table. The art of arm-wrestling, my Dada had taught me, was to read your opponent's mind and always be ready to respond at the right time. He'd been the highlander champion for the past two years, so I said a quick prayer for him to guide me.

A terrible roar started the contest and Bully made a massive effort to catch me unprepared. I was ready for this move, and like my Dada had told me, would take his best effort with as calm an expression as I could. I tried to show no strain, though my arm was quivering. I bit down hard on the peg and it saved me breath from exploding from me. Bully had the strength of his namesake, and was going red with the effort to finish me quickly. Once he knew his first effort had failed, his confidence began to ebb away and his second push lacked the power and determination of the first, so he made little progress.

I'd taken his best and now it was my turn. He knew it was coming and it showed in his face. When I made my attack, it had to be decisive or he would gain second wind, so I held back as long as I could, and took the strain. I'd always beaten Jonno at this stage, through his lack of patience. I watched Bully as he drew breath for a final try. I hit him with all I had left, and the peg between my teeth snapped as I sent his arm toward the table. You get to a point of no return in arm-wrestling when your shoulder muscles can no longer help you, and we had reached that point. The roars of my lads gave me the extra I needed, and his arm bent and shook like a tree in a hurricane. I stared him down and he was beaten.

He gave a snort as his knuckles slammed against the table, and a huge roar erupted. It was John-Joe who freed me, lifting me shoulder high and parading me around the fire as their champion.

'It takes a Scot to beat a Scot,' the tinkers were happily claiming, 'and so to the champion go the spoils.' I had my choice from the tinker camp of one of the dark-eyed girls or all I could drink. I was careful not to cause a rift by choosing a girl from the enthusiastic group that had gathered, and left it to the law of the jungle, settling for the drink. I would like to be able to say what happened next, but my memory of the events that followed is blurred by the effects of the poteen. All I can say is, I have flashing memories of heaven and that I got the sweetest smile from Isabel, a young dark-haired beauty, for some days after my recovery. Me, I was left with a permanent grin for all to see.

As normality returned, I reflected on the gamble I'd taken and the consequences had it gone wrong. I experienced a cold wave of panic. I told myself the reasons for my interference were noble, but that was a habit I would have to break, before it broke me.

A love-hate relationship was developing between the tinkers and the road gang. The tinkers became known to them, though strictly within the confines of our camp, as the dirty tinkers. They'd earned their name, so I was told, mainly because they couldn't be trusted—they'd steal and sell anything that wasn't nailed securely down. If true, I began to wonder why the company tolerated them at all.

My question was answered for me when the blasting began. They were a fearless bunch, crawling up the dark tunnels under instruction from the engineers and placing the charges, then shifting the debris from the narrow tunnels, where our lads' size was an encumbrance. It was a hazardous job and we had some near misses with rock falls and premature explosions. Injuries were becoming a common occurrence, but, thanks to God, no fatalities. Once the tunnels were clear and wide enough, my lads weighed in with picks and shovels.

We made painfully slow progress with the engineers stopping to take measurements after every blast. As a consequence we were stuck in the middle of nowhere without the anaesthetic of a pint. The men were getting discontented, fed up with the tinker poteen, which was running short and getting rougher with every new batch the tinker women made. The home-made brew was having an awful effect on those who'd had too much. Heaven alone knows what went into it, but it would send them crazy and they'd wreck the shed. I spent most of my day repairing it, which fortunately kept me away from the blasting zone, which in turn pleased Liam.

The work was hard, long and dangerous, which made for surly men. It was no surprise to me when fights broke out, the savagery of which was leaving men with more serious injuries and Liam with a dwindling workforce. Mistakes, errors of judgment, call it what you will, a mixture of the poteen and the difficult working conditions, all contributed to the lack of shoring that caused the collapse and trapped a working party deep within the tunnel.

The alarm brought Liam running and me close behind, men were staggering out with stories of a forward party trapped behind the fall, a quick role call told us that John-Joe and Mickey the Creep were both among the unfortunate group. Liam snapped into action dispatching a rescue party with himself at the head. So, with a kerchief tied tightly around my mouth, I tagged on the end to see what use I could be, though I knew if Liam had seen me I would have been sent back with a scolding. It was only the thought of my friends buried beyond a wall of stone that kept me from running back to the daylight. It was dark and oppressive like a tomb, and me like a blind man feeling his way forward. My eyes were struggling to penetrate the foggy blanket, and hearing now only the scrape of men's boots echoing back to me as I conjured up my own picture of what lay ahead.

The lamps had been extinguished by the sudden rush of air and were slowly being relit, but were making little impression. I was suffering the horrors of a slowly narrowing tunnel, where even I was being forced to bend. We ran straight into a blockage that seemed to me like an impenetrable wall.

Liam put his hand to his mouth to signal silence and when it came you could hear the flickering of the lamps. He put his ear to the wall and closed his eyes in concentration.

'I can hear something,' he said. 'It sounds like 'Danny Boy,' though I can't be sure, it could be 'When Irish eyes are smiling.'

We all looked at each other. Had Liam taken leave of his senses?

'You mean they're singing,' I said disbelievingly.

'That's just what I mean,' he smiled. 'And bless 'em they're a bit out of tune.'

'By the by what are you doing here, Georgie? This is no fit place for ye.'

He let it go and turned to face the others,

'Well then let's start moving these rocks before their voices give out.'

We formed a chain and rocks were passed back the smallest first and then the bigger ones heaved aside by the strongest men. We could all hear them now Singing and coughing in the stagnant air it seemed to give us strength and we tore at the wall with renewed vigour. Liam ordered a rest while he put his head close to the wall.

'John-Joe, are ye there? If ye are, say something, yer singings giving my lads a headache.'

"Aye, Liam, we're all here, thanks be to God, and no one's badly hurt, but we've run out of the amber nectar, so if I could trouble ye for a borrow of yer hip flask, we'd be eternally grateful.'

'They're drunk,' Liam shouted, over his shoulder. 'Ye'll get no more liquor from me till you've moved some of this stone, and if ye don't be quick, you'll have had your last drink in this life.'

It took an hour or more to gouge a hole big enough to squeeze them through but all was well and a huge cheer greeted us when we emerged.

Liam called a meeting to lay down the law: no work, no pay, no pay, no food.

A simple but effective solution, you wouldn't last long without food miles from anywhere, and I was sure he was serious. That was the bitter pill. The sweetener to go with it, to make it palatable, was his agreement to drive the wagon the ten miles on a Saturday to the pubs of Pittlochry and fetch them back, if they stayed off the poteen. It was a master stroke and good humour returned to the gang. It would be me who would be driving the wagon back, of that I had no doubt—after ten miles in a wagon, Liam would be the first to the bar.

The wagon trips back with all the crew in a paralytic stupor gave me time for reflection. I'd take myself off in my mind and talk to my family. I'd ask my Dada how I'd come this far from my plans of an education and a different life. I'd have conversations with my mother and my brothers and sisters, and wish things had been different. I'd usually end up sobbing for my family and my lost life. It helped to get it off my chest and repair my emotions. Then, and only then, could I tuck my memories away out of sight and move on. I'd tell myself that this was the means to get to England, and once there, I mustn't be tempted to stay with the gang, but have the courage to take the next step.

It took six long winter months to complete the tunnel, and by that time we'd lost four tinker men to the dynamite, one hopeless drunk to the poteen and two road men to tinker girls. It was my job now to keep those that were left from seizing up as the snows came. The work was slow and painful, and the time they lasted before they froze grew shorter. Boiling pots of water to fill the tin bath was the remedy Liam prescribed. The frozen men would warily immerse themselves fully clothed, shrieking as the steaming water penetrated their clothes and woke up the numbed flesh that lay beneath.

'It's a crude remedy alright, Georgie, but it works most of the time.'

Who was I to argue with the man who'd spent a lifetime beating everything the elements could throw at him, so I nodded, and thanked the Lord that I wasn't on the shovel, and secretly hoped I never would be.

Some were struggling to my shed, made up as a temporary hospital unable to feel their feet or take their boots off for fear of losing a toe in the struggle. So I massaged their frozen feet through their boots as best I could. The shrieks of pain as the life came creeping back into their frozen bodies was silenced by Liam's liberal doses of the whiskey.

'I'll warm the inside, while Georgie takes care of the outside,' was all he said on the matter. It seemed to work, but for how long I wasn't sure.

The weather was atrocious as we left my homeland, launching us across the border with a kick up the rear. But we'd made it and now I was on the threshold of the Promised Land. The road crossed the border into England on the seventh of December, and after six hundred miles we said our goodbyes to Scotland and I entered the unknown. School had taught me the injustices the English had visited on my clan, and had fanned the flames of hostility inside me. But as I walked across the border into England, I left Geordie McPhee-the tinker boy from Wick-behind me, and like a snake sheds its skin, I buried mine along with my past. I spent that Saturday alone with my thoughts.

I'd been too busy to think far ahead and I had never had to, my Dada had always been there and then Liam. Now I had to make my own plans and make my own mistakes, the consequences of which I'd have to learn to live with. I felt frightened and excited by this, all at the same time. This young man standing in my shoes was now George McPhee, carpenter, a person of my own invention. Why I felt the need to go to such lengths to distance myself from my roots and family, I can't say. Maybe it was the threat of disgrace or the fear of a forced marriage to Maggie and a child that would surely signal the end of my life's plan. I'll never know, but my mistakes would live with me, there would be no running away from them, of that I was sure.

This soul-searching came to a head as we laid our first mile of English road. Liam could see I was out of sorts, and over a drink or two of his famous amber nectar, I confessed my sins.

'Ah, is that all, Georgie? Sure I've sowed my seed far and wide, as they say, in every town that has a tarmacadam road, with never a backward glance. A little bit of Irish gold has been my contribution to the blood lines of my Scottish neighbours and I asked no thanks for it, though truth to tell, I've left many a grateful lassie in my wake.'

I had to smile, and I felt much relieved at the burden shared.

'Georgie, we were put on this earth to love the fairer sex, bless them, and it's up to us, the finer examples of manhood, to oblige.'

I was smiling uncontrollably now and though I knew he was exaggerating for my benefit, his humour put my own worries to flight.

I agreed to go on Saturday to a local pub and dance hall which the lads had found the previous week, where the girls were flocking to meet them. I felt much relieved and was looking forward to our outing.

There was an air of excitement by Friday when we lined up for our pay. I sat in the cabin and wrote a short letter home enclosing my usual ten shilling note. It always made me feel better that I could ease the family burden, but I never enclosed a return address, not knowing if, or when, we'd be near a town. But I'd still ask questions about everyone's health and what they were doing, knowing full well I'd receive no answer back. This one-way contact was a lifeline for my mother's sake and it let her know I was well. Truth to tell, I was afraid of news from home, at events I'd left hanging. Had Maggie had her baby? Did anyone guess my sudden disappearance was linked to her condition? I knew my father would never tell my secret, so perhaps the hue and cry had died down. For now, at least, I remained blissfully ignorant.

I took the balance of my pay to Liam, as I always did, and he put it in the safe for me. It was growing well and I felt myself a rich man by my family's standards. It was Liam's idea for me to save, and I was grateful for his advice.

'If my lads have a fault, Georgie, bless 'em, it is their generosity and if I didn't save a wee bit for them for a rainy day, they'd be stony broke by the end of the week and coming to me for a sub.'

I made no mention of his scam, that was conveniently forgotten, but now that they were receiving their full pay it was only the pubs and the local tarts that were better off.

Saturday morning was bright and crisp, and it was the day we were allowed a lie-in. The men would get their hair cut by Mickey-the-Creep, who for all his faults was pretty handy with the shears. Bristling with money and smelling of cheap perfume borrowed from the canteen ladies, we climbed into the cart. Good spirits abounded and the singing of rebel songs filled the air. A small bottle of poteen was passed around to wake the taste buds and prepare the liver for what was to come. I sat alongside Liam on the bumpy journey and it stirred vague infant memories of my wagon-ride from the Latheron workhouse.

The tiny village we came upon, tucked away in a valley, was disappointing. It looked sleepy and quiet, though I was soon to discover that a sudden invasion of people from all directions could swell the population to twice its normal size. This happened every Saturday night when the dance hall was holding a highland ceilidh, and although we were in England these people still thought of themselves as Scots.

We arrived in good spirits and the men made straight for the pub, led at a run by Liam. I left them to it, and lead the horse to the blacksmith's barn to make sure our transport was rested and well fed for the homeward journey. Then I went out to have a look around and to post my letter home. By the time I got back to the aptly named Cock Inn, arm-wrestling and story-telling were in full flow and the pints were going down in one, to cheers from the locals. Large platters of crusty bread were being wheeled out by stout-hearted girls, whose bottoms were the target for every free hand.

The landlord boasted that girls were queuing up for the Saturday shift and would fight amongst themselves to carry the platter. I was beginning to learn a little about the ways of the fairer sex, but I still had a long way to go before my hand would stray to the waitress's nether regions.

I was aglow by the time it got dark and it was time to make our way over to the dance. It was a swaying, rowdy gang that entered the hall, and with the music in full flow and with a reel whipping round at frightening speed, our boys were pulled into the dance. Part drunk I was when she grabbed me and pulled me into the fray, and heavenly it was, the feel of a woman's body beneath my hands. I smiled stupidly, unable to control my face as I was thrown around the floor by a strapping but handsome girl of about thirty. My embarrassment at being manhandled by an older woman didn't stop me enjoying it just the same.

I saw Liam out of the corner of my eye as I flew by, and I caught a glimpse of a wink at my partner, but I was in no condition to recognise that I'd been set up, so I gave myself up to the buxom wench to do whatever she pleased. Again I can't tell what happened that night, being drunk as a skunk, according to John-Joe, though how he could tell when he was horizontal in the corner for most of the evening, I'll never know. I would like to have remembered some of the pleasurable moments of my first encounter with a real woman, so I could've boasted of the details of my conquest. I only know that I was so stiff on waking that I felt like I'd been in a fight. I'd been picked up, delivered to the cart, and loaded like a sack of spuds alongside all the others, according to Liam. To hear tell, there was not one sober enough to drive the horse, and the last words that were heard were Liam's, saying, "Walk on, my beauty," before he fell asleep.

I woke slowly, still in the cart. Fragile from my exertions and minus my boots, I looked down at the holes in my socks and guessed that my boots might still be standing smartly to attention at the foot of my partner's bed.

The jolting of the cart dragged me from my thoughts and I could see that I was the first to wake. The surroundings were familiar to me with the rise of the granite hills to the left and the vast pine forest we had left behind some days before. Our old horse, bless her, had all but brought us home alone and unaided. I clambered up, took the reins, and drove the last mile, by the time we reached the camp they were all stirring. Liam was the last to move but still the first to truly wake. I was always amazed at how he could appear so fresh after a night such as we'd had, when most could hardly stand.

'Well, Georgie,' he said. 'How'd it feel to kiss the sweetest lips in Middle-Thorpe?' He gave me a conspiratorial wink. I smiled back in spite of my embarrassment.

'I wish I knew, I was too drunk to remember.'

'Then I'd best tell. Ye were a wild stallion according to big Marianne, so you were, and yer reputation will be doing the rounds in the kitchens of the Cock this morning for sure.'

I coloured up at the thought of what could have prompted such a rumour, and what I'd done with the help of Marianne's guiding hand.

'How would ye know anyway?' I said as I walked away from any more banter.

Liam called me back.

'You'll need these, Georgie,' he smiled, holding out my boots.

Glad though I was to have them back, they did add weight to his story. I scuttled off with catcalls ringing in my ears but with my head held high.

We made good progress now we'd left the mountains behind, and within a week we were out of reach of Middle-Thorpe, but now near enough to Middleton-Scrag. Here I was eager to try my new-found technique, if Liam could be believed, with the local girls. But it was not to be, the rains came down in stair rods and flooded the tracks, making them impassable and we were confined to camp. Some went back to the tinkers for poteen and the rest lurched moodily from one group to another. Me, I was like a cat on hot bricks that would have to keep on jumping for at least another week.

By the next week the rain had turned to snow, and though we worked on, our visits to town came to an end and everyone, including myself, was desperate to let our hair down. We were working in bad conditions. Road-making was twice as hard and progress was a lot slower. If Liam had offered to try to take us to town, he would have had no takers—the men were too tired from working all day in the icy wind. A warm swig of poteen and an early night were all we were fit for. Still, I had time now to settle my thoughts without the distraction of the three elements of my Irish education: hard work, hard play and recovery.

My Dada would be readying to take the family home to the Western Isles for Christmas. He'd load the cart and set off, just to keep his hand in. I'm sure it was this tonic that kept him going and kept him in touch with his roots. I wondered if my name would be the main topic of conversation. They were bound to ask the whys and wherefores of my disappearance, and sooner or later my exploits were bound to travel back via the tinkers in the next field. What would they make of my behaviour so far?

I could see Dada warning against falling into a waster's lifestyle and neglecting my books, and he'd be right, of course. I made up my mind to use my time at camp to read and write. I'd kept an account of my travels so far, which on occasions like this I would read back and see the direction that my life was taking. It seemed that my exploits, when I wrote them down, consisted of a catalogue of bad judgments. My habit of jumping in before I'd tested the water stood out clearly. I'd left out the bits that still made me blush and that I'd rather not be reminded of, but keep an account I did religiously. When I was alone I began to realise that, try as I may to learn from my mistakes, my nature seemed always to push me in the same direction and into the same pitfalls, even though I had sworn never to act without thinking and to give myself a chance to take another route.

During the next two months we only made one visit to a local town, and it only remains in the memory for the awful scrap that took place on the outskirts, in an effort to keep us out. It was a brave effort but it was never going to succeed. It would be like trying to hold back a swollen river with only your hands to help you. There were bodies lying everywhere but there was no stopping my lads and they carried me along with them.

We finally made the town and were greeted by the landlord of the pub and the girls with open arms. Clearly our reputation had preceded us and was spreading far and wide, embellished with every telling. Though tired and bloody, we were about to justify all they'd heard. The local constabulary, which consisted of two Bobbies and a sergeant, turned a blind eye. Liam had given assurances that we'd be on our way by the next morning and had greased the sergeant's hand with a healthy bribe. All the frustration of being cooped up for a month with nothing to do slid away with a continual stream of pints and the attentions of the local hussies. This time, though, I managed to avoid the attentions of the fairer sex.

It seemed I had to be totally drunk before I swung into action. I suspected that I was beginning to develop a resistance to the beer. Whether it had been watered down, as John-Joe thought, I really didn't know, but that I was still standing at the end was a mystery, while those that were too drunk to walk were carried to the cart. Homer, our faithful horse, took off at a trot, loaded to the gunnels, without any encouragement from me. When we arrived back and our mental faculties had been restored, we realised that John-Joe and Mickey-the-Creep were both missing. They may have fallen out of the cart or stopped to have a pee and been unable to catch up with Homer. We'd have to go back, or at least I would, so said Liam.

The trip back was slow, with me shouting their names and travelling carefully in case I'd run over them lying in the road. I arrived back in town to menacing looks and snide remarks when I asked for the big Irishman and his little mate. Eventually, I was pointed towards the jail house where I found them languishing, still bloodied and partially sober. According to the sergeant, they were charged with disturbing the peace, which, he informed me, carried an obligatory fine of five pounds or a week in jail.

He had a crafty look about him, this sergeant, and I could see he was after money. I had none and was stumped as to my next move. John-Joe didn't help matters by threatening to tear the door off and ram it up the sergeant's arse, if they didn't let him out. I left in search of a solution with the pleas of Mickey ringing in my ears. I'd have to think of something fast to get them out, the sooner I did, the sooner I'd get back to my bed. I left it a while and returned with a warning that the gang were on their way back and in an ugly mood, vowing they'd leave with John-Joe even if they had to take the jail apart brick by brick.

'What about yours truly?' cried Mickey.

'Well,' I said. 'If there's no jail, Mickey, there'll be nothing to hold ye.'

I was becoming an accomplished embellisher of the truth and said it with such conviction that John-Joe and Mickey were dancing a reel and promising to twist a few necks on their way out.

We finally settled for leaving quietly without any fuss, but not before we'd had one for the road.

The trouble with reputations is that you are stuck with them, even if you just wanted a quiet drink. We were met by those who were glad to see our money and those who wanted to run us out of town. We seemed to attract the ladies all right, but this naturally rankled their men and was a good recipe for a fight, so it kept the scrappers amongst us happy. I began to find it all a bit wearisome— just work, play, scrap and sleep—so I took to my books. John-Joe, bless him, thought I was ill and came to see me.

'Georgie, I have the cure-all me old mother gave to me, and it's painless if you take it quick.' He produced a concoction of spirits that looked deceptively like water, but knowing John-Joe, I wouldn't like to say what was in it.

'It's an all or nothing, kill or cure, boy, and I swear by it.'

'No thanks, John-Joe, I just need a rest from the excitement and to catch up on me learning.'

'There's gratitude for ye,' he said, knocking it back in one, and turning purple as it scorched its way past his adam's apple. 'I've never been one for the wasting of good liquor,' he croaked. 'I'll be off then and I'll say hello to the ladies for you'

It had never crossed John-Joe's mind how they'd make it back with only Liam and the horse to rely on (and of the two, the horse would get my vote). That was in the future and John-Joe lived only in the present.

I sat back in the peace of the cabin with my kerosene lamp and started to read. It was just a penny novel I'd picked up somewhere but the practice was good for me. After a few chapters my brain was creaking, so I let my mind wander back over the border to my family's home.

What would they be doing? Where was that rascal Jonno? Had Charlie taken my advice and gone to work for Angus? How were Jeannie and Hughie? All questions I had no answers to, and with no news I felt like the forgotten man sheltering under a dark cloud. The thought that I'd never know anything of the rise or fall of my family's fortunes made the loneliness that surrounded me at that moment unbearable. I closed my eyes and my past came flooding back, but the pictures I saw in my mind were the same pictures. I'd have no new memories of family life, they would always be the same ones replayed over and over. My dreams were now populated by new characters. It was like starting a new book before finishing the last one. I was getting maudlin and shifted irritably. I should have gone to town with the others and drowned my sorrows. I decided instead to walk over to the tinker camp. I knew a few of them, and just at this moment I needed some of my own kind.

I found them sitting around a fire, swapping stories of how they'd come to travel without land or possessions. I felt comfortable squatting there by the fire and looking around at the faces of the men, flickering in the firelight. They seemed to be friendly enough and they surely didn't deserve the reputation of being untrustworthy rogues. I had to take as I found. After all, who was I to judge anyone? A runaway who'd left his mess for someone else to clear up. The poteen came round and a warm glow filled my stomach.

'You're Georgie McPhee,' said the old man, pointing at me, his wrinkled face the colour of old teak and creased like yesterday's newspaper. I nodded as they all looked my way. I'd heard all about old man Rags and the dog he called Bones from the tinker girls. You wouldn't need three guesses as to what his profession was, and he looked and smelled like something that belonged on his own cart. Rags ruled his girls with a rod of iron and they obeyed his every wish without as much as a word. His reputation with a knife was legendary and his people tiptoed carefully around him.

'I know yer father, Robbie, and uncle Will and their father, old Isaac the crockery dealer. I could tell ye stories of the McPhees of Conolsay and their legendary chieftain whose followers were eventually driven from their lands. It's a sad piece of history, Georgie, all that's left is a statue of the clan chief on the island as a tribute to them all.'

I felt a glow of pride spread through me and promised myself there and then to go and see it for myself and learn about the history that brought us to our present plight.

'Were we land-owners then, Rags?' I asked.

'Ye were, Georgie, and a powerful and fierce clan yer descended from—the Irish O'Fees some say, mixed with a measure of Viking, tricked and betrayed by worthless lowland Scots in ti the hands of the British and forced to wander.'

I felt a kinship with these tinkers almost like my own family group, and thanks to the continual passing of the poteen, I was beginning to get fuddled. From somewhere music started and a dark haired beauty began to dance. Rags took this opportunity to take a long drink from the bottle, and passed it on. I could see it would soon be back to me, and although fuddled, I was still able enough to halt my slide into oblivion, by sticking my tongue in the neck and pretending to take a long swig.

'That's it Georgie,' Rags growled, 'taken like a true tinker.'

I waved drunkenly at him, and giggled like an idiot. I forced my eyes to focus on the dancers long shapely legs, and with her spinning like a top, they were now in full view, her feet were stamping and her hands clapping the gipsy rhythm, I had seen the gypsy dancing at the gathering on the Western Isles and it had always excited me, but try as I may, my blurred eyes had trouble making out her features. But her flashing smiles sent quivers up my spine, and the more so because I felt they were meant for me. The shouts of encouragement and clapping hands that accompanied her around the fire finally petered out, and her dance ended sooner than I would have liked. She faded out of the fire light and into the gloom, with my eyes following, searching the blackness for one last glimpse. My breathing gradually returned to normal, and my heart finally stopped pounding, but as I returned to face the roving bottle, a last disappointment registered in my involuntary sigh.

Was I dreaming or was it the drink? Had I felt something warm squeezing next to me? The heat from her soft body had gradually reawakened me and now I was fully aware of her presence, the heat from the fire, the poteen and her body conspired to make me sweat.

I could see out of the corner of my eye it was the dark-eyed beauty, Isabel, who'd been my table wrestling prize, and had danced for us this very night and I remembered the invite she'd given me.

'Georgie, ye came then, and did ye like my dance?' She whispered. I nodded like my head was loose.

'Will ye come for a walk wi me then?

'Leave him be, girl,' said Rags, 'the boy's got some drinking to do.' She persisted, which I thought was very unwise.

'Ye could take me to Liam's cabin, Georgie. He's got a cot, so the girls tell me.'

She had a beautiful smile and I stared hopelessly into her dark eyes and felt myself wanting to do whatever she asked, but I was loath to leave with such obvious intent.

'She's a persistent little hussy, that one, like her mother,' Rags grunted.

'Be off with ye, Isabel, or ye'll feel me belt.' She pulled a face but slunk away without another word.

The poteen came round again, but with every swig, I grew more excited. My eyes followed her departure and I found myself wishing I was going with her. I could see she was lingering in the shadows at the edge of the camp, and with the poteen making me reckless, I made my excuses to have a pee and wandered over to where she lurked just outside the range of the firelight. She pulled me back into the trees, and with her face against mine, and her hot breath brushing my ear, she whispered.

'Have ye the key to Liam's cabin, Georgie? I'm desperately in need of a good man.'

I was flushed, a little drunk and excited fit to bust. I think I would have performed any task for her at that moment, but I hadn't got Liam's key, though I did know where he kept it.

Visions of Maggie floated before my eyes, reminding me of the feel of her soft, smooth skin and the excitement that caused me so much trouble. But try as I may, the poteen had my wits and I was under her spell.

'Georgie!' Rags shouted. 'It's your turn for the bottle.'

I nodded to Isabel and she kissed me long and hard.

'Hurry back, pretty boy, if ye want some more of the same.'

I tore myself away and stumbled back flushed and fumbling with my trousers to make my errand look real. I was glad none present could read, for my thoughts, I was sure, were written clearly all over my face. The bottle was waiting as I sat down, and I took a large swig that made my head swim. As I tried to pass it on, I felt myself begin to topple. I was righted by a strong arm and made a supreme effort to pay attention, Rags was still talking to me.

'Yer Liam's right-hand man now then, Georgie,' he said, 'and privy to all his little secrets.'

'Aye,' I said, nodding my head.

'They say he's been creaming a little off the top from all of us for a long time. He must be worth a fortune, but I have to admire him for that. He's cleverer than he looks, that's for sure.'

Your tongue can run away from your good sense when you're drunk, and mine had a life of its own. It wagged away, releasing all my private memories. They had Liam's complete scam, and how I managed to right it for the gang, in one long, rambling confession.

'Ye didn't right it for us though, yer own kind eh, Georgie?'

I hadn't thought that Liam had pulled the same stroke on the tinkers, but they did and there were some hard faces around the fire. But I was too far gone to worry.

'Liam O'Donahue is the finest Irishman in the whole world and he's my friend and protector and I won't hear a word against him, I said defiantly.

'I admire loyalty in a man, even if he is protecting a thief against his own.'

Those around the fire growled in protest but Rags held up his hand.

'Georgie was only doing what a good tinker would do—standing by a friend. Ye'd better get off to Isabel, before ye pass out all together,' he laughed.

I didn't need telling twice, even though I had trouble standing and even more trouble walking. I zigzagged my way to the place I'd left her, and fell into her arms.

'Uhh, ye smell like the inside of a dirty tinker's boot, boy.'

I righted myself and tried hard to gather a bit of dignity.

'I'm all right, Isabel. I'm just feeling happy.'

'Well, how about feeling me instead? I've been waiting for you all night.'

I made a drunken grab at her but she avoided me.

'I'm freezing now, so I'll not be taking me clothes off outside,' she said, pushing me away.

'So if ye really want me, ye can take me to Liam's cabin—it's that or nothing at all. They say he has the softest cot. Say ye will, Georgie.'

Like a dummy I said it. 'I will, I will.'

As we left, I heard Rags' voice call out. 'Where're ye going, Isabel?'

'Ti heaven, Dada, wit Georgie,' she squealed.

I was to remember her words and the way her finger traced a line down my spine, like a stiletto finding my soft spot. Nor would I forget the sight of her beautiful body above me and the black curls tickling my chest as she took me to heaven and left me to see the devil. It was still dark when I woke, my head was splitting and I was feeling cold enough to die.

I struggled up and found myself staring at the open door of Liam's cabin and what was left of the interior. I stared dumbly at the mess, my mouth miming her name, though it was clear to me that I was alone. My eyes traversed the carnage. What could have caused such devastation under my very nose? I closed my eyes and shook my head again, trying in my own desperate way to put things back in their proper order. I remained like that for maybe a minute, not wanting to open them to find that nothing had changed. The hot tears trickled down my cheeks as I released my lids and let them rise. The horror was still there and now I knew I'd have to face it. Somewhere in the back of my mind I already knew the purpose of the destruction, but until now I had not wanted to face it.

Liam's safe was gone. They'd taken a time to find it, hence the destruction. Would that they'd just asked me where it was and saved the wreckage, but I knew I wouldn't have told willingly. I moved around in despair. Why couldn't they have beaten me? Or tied me up, at least? They could have left a victim, instead of leaving a fool. They'd left me with not a mark to my face to tell Liam that his hard-earned money was in the hands of the dirty tinkers. Me and my own savings were, for the second time, parted by a woman, but I wasted no sympathy on myself. I deserved no better. The women who populated my life seemed to be calculating bitches after one thing and I was falling over myself to help them get it.

I burned with anger at my humiliation. I'd been spoiled by a mother's love and trusted their good intentions, but I'd have to harden up or before too long I'd be in the poor house. As I sat there shaking my head, I heard the cart crunching up the road. I wanted nothing more than to run and hide, anything but face Liam with the news. I knew I'd have to go outside and prepare him for the worst, so, with my heart in my mouth I stumbled through the open door.

I could see now the empty field where the tinkers had camped and where I'd sat last night feeling so happy. They'd gone, leaving their litter fluttering in the breeze, the smouldering embers of last night's fire and 'yours truly.' I stood in a trance, watching as the cart came with no one at the reins and a pile of bodies sprawled in the back. I caught myself limping as if I'd put up a fight, my mind conjuring up an automatic defence, but Liam would see through it. I'd let them in, given that little vixen the door key. I'd been too drunk to give her any more information so they'd set about tearing the place apart, as much in spite as in an effort to find the hidden safe key. They'd finally ripped the cast-iron safe from its mountings, carried it off, and now were long gone.

Homer came to a stop beside me and stirrings from the cart told me I was seconds away from becoming homeless, jobless and friendless. Liam would be the first to rise, he always was, and it pained me to wait while he slowly raised himself. I stood frozen as he stared blearily out of his one remaining eye, the other being closed and purple in colour. He had a cut above it that had leaked blood down the side of his face. His injury was testament to a successful night out and would be the least of his problems.

'Is that you, Georgie? Ah, ye missed a great night, so you did. We had a minor scrap with the locals who tried to ban us from the ceilidh but they changed their minds, bless'em, and we had a real knees-up.'

'Liam,' I broke in, unable to stand the tension. 'I have something to tell ye and I don't know how to begin…'

'I may only have one eye, Georgie, but I can see, as plain as day, that the tinkers have scarpered.'

'They've run off with your safe and all the money, and it's my fault. I thought they were my friends.' I stood waiting for the explosion to come.

'If you'd been around tinkers, of the dirty variety, as long as I have, Georgie, ye learn to leave nothing to chance.'

'But they wrecked your cabin and found the safe, while I slept with the temptress Isabel on your cot.'

'It's a nice cot, don't ye think? They didn't take it, did they? If they had, I'd be after them with all guns blazing.'

'No! Liam, you're not listening, you're still drunk. It's the safe they've taken and all our money.'

'Oh that,' he said, 'I never leave camp without emptying my safe, Georgie, and Homer looks after the money, the little darling. Just in case I'm incapable, you see. All they took was an empty safe, and without the key,' he said, dangling it from his watch-chain, 'they'll have the devil's own job to open it.'

I couldn't believe what I was hearing. My face crumpled and my eyes filled with tears of relief.

'I'm not forgetting that yer lustful nature was responsible for me wrecked home, so I'll expect ye to put that right first thing,' he laughed.

The others were stirring and I took a deep breath. There was an important lesson to learn about the lengths some people will go to for money, though whether it would harden me up, I wasn't at all sure.

I worked hard to restore Liam's cabin and he said nothing to anyone about my lapse in good sense. They took my work of refurbishing the interior as one of Liam's fancies. The tinkers were no loss now the tunnelling was finished. Liam was about to pay them off now that the mountains were behind us, so I put the incident behind me, too, but I couldn't help marvelling that Liam seemed always to be one step ahead of the game.

I'd give my books another try fiction had to be a lot safer than life on the open road. We were well into England now and it seemed every bit the same as home. I'm not sure what I expected but the mention of England conjured up images of fancy houses and fancy people, but up to now the only difference was their accent and the weather. It was considerably warmer here, so in that respect the work was more pleasant. John-Joe, though, was suffering with frostbite since the very cold snap caught us coming through the mountains, and some of his toes and fingers had very little feeling. It was my job to treat him to hot tubs and massage some life back into them, and slowly but surely, they were coming alive.

For now, though, Mickey-the-Creep was his constant companion and would hold John-Joe's full pint until it was half empty and then John-Joe could manage to lift it himself. It was difficult for them, not being so used to the severe conditions that could blow in from the North Sea. I'd gone to school barefoot in winter to save my boots, and the wearing of gloves was a luxury we seldom had.

I remembered my swim in the river from which I almost died, but thank God, I have never suffered like poor John-Joe from frostbite.

He was a big loss on the shovel, but he was still up for the scraps, his hands didn't stop him wading in and I'd have the job of putting him right. He'd get Mickey to close his fist before a fight and prize them open again afterwards. He wasn't as light on his feet now, with frozen toes to slow him down, so he would get caught with a sledgehammer blow, more often than he should and his face was beginning to show the signs of battle.

I spent more time with my books and I read to John-Joe while he nursed one of Liam's bottles, when I could persuade him to stay away from town. We were both becoming Western fans, so each time Liam went to town he'd bring me back a penny Western and I'd go off in my dreams to a different place where the sun shone non-stop and everything turned out the way it was supposed to. I'd close my eyes and let my imagination take me anywhere and everywhere, while John-Joe snored loudly.

I knew the time was drawing near when I should leave and strike out on my own, but I kept putting the decision back. Perhaps the next town, I'd tell myself, but when it came, I'd find some excuse to stay. I'd always known it would be hard, but if I didn't go, I'd be in danger of becoming as rootless as my Irish friends. I searched my diary for words of comfort, and for a clue to confirm my decision. Dada's words came back to steady me.

'Geordie,' he'd said, 'you're different, ye can be whatever ye want, if ye have the courage to try.'

My life had changed when I went to live on the farm with Angus and I was rewarded with the chance to take up the tools and learn to make or mend. Again, when I left Wick, I had to grow up fast to make my way among men, and I learned though none too quickly, how to fight, drink, and enjoy the pleasures of wanton women. The next time I leave, I promised myself, it would be to put down roots and start to climb the ladder of respectability.

I was in my fourth year away by now and I was just coming up nineteen. I longed for the family life I'd left behind, even with the hardship it brought, but that was gone forever. There would be no going back. Dada had said there would be no future for me in the back streets of Wick and I wasn't born to the tinker life like Jonno. Again I found myself resenting my background. In England, if people knew I was a tinker, they'd treat me as second class, so I resolved again never to mention it to anyone. It wasn't that I was ashamed of my own family, but tinkers carried a stigma that could hold you back, though I wished with all my heart it wasn't so.

Dada had said I had tinker blood running through my veins and I should be proud of it, but I was about to ignore his wisdom and deny my own heritage. I don't think I had ever felt so alone as at that moment when I buried my past, my own flesh and blood, in favour of a new life. The tears for my lost family flowed down my cheeks for the last time.

Now I must find somewhere to settle, start a family of my own, and forget all that had gone before. I had to shove myself, right or wrong, in the direction I wanted my life to go if I were to realise my dream, make good my mother's vow at my birth and make my Dada proud of me. They were three good reasons that helped me to tear myself away from my lads.

§

Chapter Seven

The Griffin Girls

'Mother, there's a young man, a George McPhee, at the door. He's come to see the room.'

'He's gorgeous,' Mary mimed to her sisters. They stopped what they were doing and stared around the door.

'You girls get on and don't you go making a spectacle of yourselves, or you'll have me to answer to.' I stood at the door with the paper advertising a room to let in the small village of Bircham, Norfolk. I'd put on the new suit I'd bought from a charity shop in King's Lynn and it fitted me like a glove. They do say that clothes maketh the man and I must say I was pleased with the result. I looked a new man and it gave me confidence. With a tan from working outside and my father's black hair, I was making an impression on the first girl I'd met.

A sweet smile of invitation had greeted me on my second rap on the door. Mickey-the-Creep had cut my hair free on my last day and he had made a good job of it. So when I left with my pockets full of my savings from Liam's new safe and with a bit more besides, bless'em, there wasn't a dry eye in the place. It looked ridiculous watching grown men cry. I'd seen them in pain and heartbroken, but they'd never shed a tear until now. They'd tried to make me stay, but fate had marked my card and this was the crossroads, a now or never decision to stay or go—and go I must. We all cried like a nursery full of babies and a part of my heart went with them when I moved on.

So here I was, standing on a doorstep, lost in thought, facing a homely looking woman with a face that had family written all over it.

'You'll be George McPhee then, come to see the room. Well, you'd best come in and don't forget to wipe your feet,' she added.

I followed her down the hall, furnished with a hat-stand and cabinet polished to perfection and smelling of lavender, to a little room at the back of the house. It was so neat but she still looked back at me for my approval. I nodded obligingly.

'It's very nice, Mrs Griffin,' I said, trying to make some kind of impression.

'It's only small, Mr McPhee, but it's clean,' she said, waiting for me to agree.

She seemed to need confirmation of how well she kept her place and would keep a silence until she got it.

'It's not what I've been used to, I'll say that, but it'll do very nicely thank you, Mrs Griffin.'

If she had known what I had been used to, I would have been frog-marched straight out of the door. How strange it felt to be in a room of my own with a proper bed and somewhere to hang my clothes, curtains at the window and an electric light that filled the room like daylight.

She broke into my thoughts with a list of rules as long as your arm.

'I'll have no strong drink and no unruly behaviour. You will, I hope, attend church on Sunday with the rest of the family, I won't have heathen living in my house. Breakfast is at seven and tea at six. The rent will be one pound, paid promptly on a Friday. I lock the door at ten and won't be disturbed, so you'll be in by half past nine. My girls are lively and wicked, as all young girls are, so be warned and keep your distance, until I know you better.' All through, I just nodded my agreement and smiled sweetly.

There was a knock and Mrs Griffin pulled the bedroom door open. There framing the door, were three of the prettiest faces you could wish to see, all smiling sweetly at me whilst talking to their mother.

'Is there anything we can do for you, Mother?' They said in harmony, still looking at me. I gave them the once over, as Liam called it, and flashed each one my best smile. They were all as dark-haired as me but pale-skinned, it was a beautiful combination and they all had lovely smiles.

'These are three of my six daughters. At the top is Mary, then Ellen and Norah. Lillian, the oldest, married a soldier and followed him to London, more fool her. Violet married a monster, and Evelyn, the youngest, is in bed. I also have four sons, two of which have left. Will followed Lillian to London, and Jock's training as a gamekeeper at the Sandringham estate. Len and Laurie have gone to choir practice, so you'll meet them soon enough.'

She was proud of her family, and unlike me, she would hide nothing. She shooed the girls out and down the stairs. I could hear them giggling all the way down.

I stretched out on the bed and surveyed my kingdom, picked up the paper and reread the war news. I'd been posted to the Bircham Newton Aerodrome to build planes in a hurry, as a war seemed just around the corner. What the outcome of this conflict would be, heaven alone knew, but the taste of tattie pie, and the depression, cold and hunger that accompanied the Great War, stirred in the depths of my mind. That was the war to end all wars, they said. So why were we back on the brink of disaster?

It was a question I was unable to answer. It couldn't have come at a worse time for me. I'd finally found my feet and was ready to settle while all about me was in confusion. The tinker in me rose to the surface at times like this and I wanted to take off into the wilderness, like Dada's family had, and leave everybody else to sort it out. But, like my Dada, would I be too proud to run?

The sound of clinking china and the sweet smell of home-cooking drifting down the hall rescued me from my thoughts and brought me back to the present, chasing away unpleasant memories of another time, another life. I hovered on the edge of my bed for the call to tea, while I counted out my rent money and had it ready. I had a feeling I would score some points with Mrs Griffin if I paid in advance, and I was going to show her that I was a trustworthy and good lodger.

It crossed my mind, while I was waiting for tea, how I could best avoid any in-depth probing about my background. I thought it best to be as truthful as possible just in case a little white lie crept up and caught me unawares. Most of my life could've been lived as a town boy, so I'd just leave out the tinker bits.

'George,' a sweet voice called, followed by a knocking.

I almost fell out of the door on top of Mary, or was it Ellen, or Norah? I couldn't be sure.

'I won the right to come and fetch you,' she said, giving me her best smile. 'I'm Mary, the best-looking one,' she added with a wink. 'We played the stone, scissors and paper game, and I won,' she said triumphantly. 'Ellen always favours paper and Norah the scissors, so here I am. Oh, by the way, your tea's ready.'

'Mary, I could eat a horse and still have room for pudding, so lead on.' I followed Mary down the stairs. I'd be the object of everybody's attention, I expected that, and sure enough everything went quiet and all faces turned towards me.

'This is George McPhee and he's Scottish, aren't you, George?' Mary announced.

'A highlander for my sins,' I said, nodding to everyone around the table.

'Sit down here, George,' said Norah, patting the empty space between herself and Ellen.

'That's not fair! That's my place,' Mary snapped.

'You can sit between Len and Laurie,' Norah said with a satisfied smile. 'We all know how you like the boys.'

All this was going over my head. There seemed to be quite a bit of infighting going on.

'Why don't I sit with the two boys and Mary can have her seat back?' I squeezed myself between the two boys and nodded to both.

'Good idea,' Mrs Griffin said, over her shoulder. 'It's nice to have a peacemaker in the house.'

Mary and Norah were looking daggers at each other, claiming the other had started the pinching under the table, while Ellen looked the picture of sweet innocence.

'We'll have all hands above the table if you please, and show me if they're clean,' Mrs Griffin said, without turning around. All hands appeared as if she had eyes in the back of her head. She clearly wasn't a lady to trifle with. After a summary look, she dismissed them one at a time back to the bathroom to scrub them to her satisfaction.

'Fetch me the jar of mustard from the kitchen cupboard Nora, and dip your fingers in it. I'll put a stop to your filthy habits. What decent boy's going to look at a girl with nails bitten down to the quick.'

'I haven't been biting them,' she said, poking her tongue out at her mother's back.

'I broke them climbing the tree in the garden to fix the rope swing.'

It made no difference to Mrs Griffin, I could see that. Nora was going to get the mustard treatment anyway, guilty or not.

'And don't poke your tongue out at me my girl,' she said, 'or you'll be getting a slap.'

You could have heard a pin drop. I'd walked into something here and I didn't know quite what to make of it.

Mrs Griffin slammed a huge pot on to the table, smelling of fresh vegetables and another of potatoes. The meat consisted of small shreds in thick gravy and a home-made loaf. This was a banquet compared to home, and a whole lot more nourishing than the canteen food I'd been eating on the road.

'You can dish the plates out, Mary, and Ellen the knives and forks. Norah, you can get some water for George. You boys, are your hands clean now?'

They nodded that they were.

I was sure mine wouldn't pass her test, so I made my excuses and left. By the time I came back, there was a plate in my place with two slices of meat on it and it drew envious looks from the rest.

I felt embarrassed at the inaudible mumbling from the others and it confirmed my suspicions, that I was the only one in line for the meat. Mrs Griffin sensed the atmosphere and responded straight away.

'George pays his way here, and when you do, you'll be entitled. Until then there's plenty of potatoes to fill you up.'

I kept silent. There didn't seem to be anything I could say that would rectify the situation, but I managed to eat it without saying how delicious it was. The meal over, the others scattered to see to their various jobs, leaving me and Mrs Griffin at the table. I could feel it coming, the probing, the satisfying of her curiosity as to how I'd come to Norfolk and why. I broke the silence with a compliment on her cooking skills. That, to my limited knowledge, would usually put the women in your corner, but Mrs Griffin wasn't to be so easily satisfied. After-all, she did have three lovely daughters to keep in line and an unattached man she knew nothing about.

'Now, tell me about yourself, George, so I can know the kind of man who lives under my roof.'

She'd have chapter and verse on me, before I'd have permission to leave the table and there'd better not be any gaps in my life story or she would assume the worst.

I kept it vague and uninteresting, and hoped that I had bored her sufficiently to allay any fears. I hadn't heard mention of their father, but I assumed he wasn't about to walk through the door for whatever reason.

'My husband died last year, George, if you're wondering,' she said, reading my mind yet again. 'Ernest was only fifty-two and never had a day's illness in his life,' she added with a weariness that told me she still found his death hard to believe. I was, I could see, the lifeline she needed to make ends meet and I warmed to this woman who faced bringing up her six remaining children on her own, battling each day to keep the wolf from the door.

'Mrs Griffin, if I can help, I'd like to. I can make and mend anything and my money will always be on time,' I said, counting my pound on to the table.

'Thank you George, It'll help me to keep my children at home, for company and to help me with Evelyn. Evelyn's my youngest daughter and she's in bed right now.'

I carried on with my version of my life up to the present, the joining of the road gang that had brought me eventually to King's Lynn. My work at a furniture shop in the town, where I'd hardly started when I received my call-up papers. I subsequently failed my medical, I told her, having had rheumatic fever as a boy, so the Ministry of Works sent me here to work at the aerodrome, building planes during the day and to be on call if needed by the home guard at night.

'Another war,' she sighed. 'Is it possible we learned nothing from the last one? Am I to lose my sons in some foreign place?' She shook her head in disbelief.

'Maybe it won't come to anything, it's too soon to know,' I said, trying to reassure her.

'Ernest was exempt from the last one,' she continued, as if I hadn't spoken.

'He was kept back to work on the Queen's estate. But it caused him to work himself to an early grave. There seems no place for peace on this earth, so we must take our pleasure while and where we can, George.'

She shrugged then, realizing she'd been sidetracked and she gave me a frown.

'You keep your cards close to your chest, but I'm a pretty good judge and I'm handy with the rolling pin, so be warned. My girls seem to have taken a liking to you, so I'll expect you to treat them with respect. The boys will follow your example, them being that much younger and without a father to guide them. So if you're to stay here, you have a lot to live up to.'

I couldn't believe my luck. I was being invited to join the family and I couldn't think of a nicer family to be part of. I went to bed without that lonely feeling that had been part of my life since I left home, and I slept a dreamless sleep. I rose early to walk the mile or so to work, and found Mrs Griffin was already busy at work in the kitchen, lighting the fires, and preparing breakfast.

I could see many similarities in our families: the children top-n-tailed, so I could have a room to myself, her children having to be hired out to make the money go round. They were poor through no real fault of their own, but they weren't short of food—like my Dada they lived off the land. They caught rabbits, poached pheasants, and grew all their own vegetables, which was a great relief. You can stand any other form of deprivation as long as you don't go hungry. They all seemed healthy and happy and didn't seem to resent me, so I'd passed the first test and landed squarely on my feet.

Four of her own children had already left, and the remaining six were squashed into two small bedrooms to make room for me, whatever else she was, Mrs Griffin was a practical woman but I suspected that she would shed a few tears into her pillow at what might have been, had her Ernest not been such a selfless man.

The girls told me that they had moved from Shernborne when the farm manager their father had worked so conscientiously for had moved to Bircham and wanted his best man to follow. Ernest packed them and all their possessions into his cart and his two beloved horses hauled them the two miles to their new home. His favourite horse made straight back for his stable in Shernborne, and Ernest, without any hesitation, had walked the two miles back to fetch him. He rode the sweating horse back again and caught a chill. Within no time it turned to fever and the loving husband and father unexpectedly died of pneumonia, leaving a grief-stricken wife and ten children.

I pondered this on my way to work. The one glaring difference between our families was respectability. My Dada was respected by all who knew him, but shunned by those who didn't. He was tainted by his tinker blood, whereas Mrs Griffin was from farming stock. She was one level above us on the ladder of respectability. It was all right to be poor, as long as you weren't tinkers. I apologised to Dada as I strode up the Bircham road. What would he think of me denying my heritage? He always said that ye canny measure a man by the cut of his clothes, and here I was doing just that. I was still wrestling with my conscience when I arrived at the gates of the airfield and joined a line of men filing in.

'Name!' the guard snapped.

'George McPhee,' I said, giving him my papers from the ministry.

'Carpenters to the left, report to Gus MacCloud at hangar four.' He waved me on, handing me a name tag that I attached, like everybody else, to my jacket.

'You a chippy then, mate?' a voice said beside me.

'Who wants to know?'

'Steady, George,' he said, squinting at my name tag. 'My name's Shanny, Mr Francis to you,' he said, smiling. He put out his hand and we shook. I gave his hand a squeeze, and he squeezed back.

'Quite a handshake you've got there, George boy,' he said, giving his fingers a shake.

Liam had taught me that your first handshake would signal that you were a person to be reckoned with, and the more painful your grip, the higher you rose up the pecking order. 'Scrapping your way up, Georgie' he'd said, 'is a lot more painful.'

He'd made me practise the technique with the gang until I could see the respect in their eyes.

This Shanny was a cheerful man, about my age but taller and thinner with a shock of unruly fair hair.

'Aye, I'm a carpenter,' I said. 'And you?'

'For me sins,' he said. 'Although, I admit, I don't know much about building planes. The only ones I've built, that flew, were made of newspaper. Where you staying then, George, if you don't mind me asking?'

'I'm billeted with Mrs Griffin and her three beautiful daughters in the village. She cooks like a dream and keeps her place spotless,' I said, feeling that he couldn't better that.

'You're a very lucky man, George. I'm billeted with an old biddy who can't cook and lives in a hovel. I don't suppose this Mrs Griffin would have room for a little one?'

'I'll ask her for you, I'm sure she'd welcome the money.'

We had arrived at hangar four, and we moved inside. The place was heaving with men and the noise was deafening. Planes were in various stages of construction, some with skins on and others just skeletons.

'Mr MacCloud!' Shanny shouted over the noise of hammering. A man's head popped out of the underbelly of what turned out to be a Hurricane and signalled us to come to him.

'Mr Francis and Mr McPhee at your service, plane builders of renown,' Shanny said.

'A comic eh? Well ye'll be too tired ti crack jokes by the time I'm finished with ye.'

It seemed strange to hear another Scottish accent and a bit worrying.

The McPhees were a well-known tinker clan and he may put two and two together and come up with four. The MacClouds were lowland Scots and not partial to highlanders, so I'd steer clear of reminiscing with him. Anyway, he seemed much too busy to concern himself with names.

'Follow me,' he snapped, and led us to a far corner of the hangar where we were introduced to a foreman in charge of a small group, working on a biplane. Mr MacCloud left and took no further interest in us. The foreman handed me a blueprint, as if I should know what it was, and asked if I had any experience of aeronautical work.

'A little,' I said. I couldn't tell him that my experience was limited to mending sheds, gates and general repairs. Fortunately Shanny jumped in and saved the day.

'No problem. You leave it to me and George.'

'Ye two can work on section A3 of the wing and make sure ye follow the specifications.'

It had never occurred to me that if you called yourself a carpenter that they expected you to be formally trained. I soon realised that a make or mend plane wasn't going to be good enough for a pilot to risk his life in.

'Shanny,' I whispered, 'I can't read these plans.'

'Just follow yours truly and you can't possibly go wrong. You just concentrate on the important things, like getting me billeted with Mrs Griffin's delectable daughters.'

Despite all his comedy, Shanny was an expert craftsman and my head ached with concentration following his instructions. I was good with the tools, had a feel for the timber, and had a good eye for levels and angles. I just needed to learn to interpret the symbols that covered the drawings. To me, it looked like spiders had left their footprints all over them, but I was keen to learn.

The first morning left my head spinning, and when the hooter went for lunch, I was more than grateful. We traipsed off to the canteen to get a large mug of tea and a roll with a great slab of cheese holding it open. I doubted I could open my mouth wide enough for this monster, but I was hungry enough to try. We took ourselves outside to where we could watch one of our newly built planes taxiing down the runway. The large bomb slung underneath gave it the look of a pregnant whale, and it seemed to be having trouble gaining speed. I was sure I could have run faster. I was puzzled, as I watched it struggle past in slow motion, as to how it was going to get off the ground. It continued to limp to the end of the runway and pointed its nose in the direction of the sky. It only just cleared the grass but the pilot seemed determined to keep going. It rose but never looked comfortable, and before it reached ten feet, it thumped back down and keeled over with a breaking sound. We dived for cover, expecting the bomb to explode, but nothing happened.

A rescue crew raced to the scene and carried the pilot from the wreck and raced away again, all with well-practised speed. The bomb blew as they rounded the hangar and it left a huge crater in the field, scattering wood the size of matchsticks into the air. My ears were ringing from the explosion as the debris rained down on the hangar roof. The hooter sounded and we made our way back to hear Mr MacCloud spouting angrily that it took his whole crew several weeks, flat out, to build the bloody thing and one man five minutes to demolish it. We looked at each other and Shanny smothered a smile.

'Look on the positive side, Mr MacCloud, at least we know the bomb works.'

'We'll have to make bigger planes or fit smaller bombs,' I added. It seemed like the obvious solution to me, but just drew a scowl from the dour Scotsman.

'No,' he said. 'We'll have ti make them twice as bloody fast, so ye'll all be getting a belly full of unpaid overtime, how's that?' he said, and stormed off to get his plan rubber-stamped.

'I'm afraid you've started off on the wrong foot there, George my boy. Life could be difficult for you on the dark side of Mr MacCloud.'

We worked non-stop all afternoon and when the hooter finally sounded, it was none too soon for me. I gathered my tools, stripped off my overalls and looked forward to a bit of Mrs Griffin's home-cooking.

Mr MacCloud's voice came loud and clear, over the speaker, as we headed for the door.

'Five minutes for a cuppa, lads, and then back here double-quick.'

You could've heard a pin drop. Nobody moved for a second… then a sudden rush for the canteen. The watch was ticking and Mr MacCloud had his beady eye on it.

I slurped the hot tea, burning my mouth for my trouble, and we filed back to be told that the ministry had asked for an extra shift for the war effort, unpaid of course, and that Mr MacCloud had agreed on our behalf. For once, Shanny had nothing to say, so we set about our work with determination and I put thoughts of my dinner on hold.

It was a long four hours, but I felt that I'd done my bit for the lads who'd be risking their lives on the battle front. A feeling of exhaustion couldn't be compared to facing death and destruction on some battlefield far from home. We walked the mile or so back home, dog-tired and hungry enough to eat a horse. I left Shanny, promising that if I had anything to do with it, it would be his last fish pie and that I'd be sure to ask Mrs Griffin if he could share my room.

As I reached the door, I was met by a stony stare. This wasn't the time to make my request, so I just smiled and said, 'Good evening.'

'Your dinner will be ruined, Mr McPhee,' she said, giving me a sniff, to check my whereabouts. It was no longer George so I knew she suspected the worst. I was sure she would have the nose of a gun dog when it came to the scent of beer, and if I'd come from the pub, my dinner would have been scraped into the bin and me with it.

'You're looking tired George, get washed up and I'll heat it up.'

We sat on our own at the table, the girls were in bed and the boys would soon be. I ate my dinner with my eyes drooping, and visions of having fallen asleep at the table with Angus came to mind. Another minute and I would be gone.

'Get yourself off to bed now, George, you look beat.'

She sounded just like my mother. I went to bed with thoughts of her in my mind, and in my dreams I scurried my way back to Wick.

I slept like a log, and had Mrs Griffin not called me, I'd have been there still.

It was Ellen who served my breakfast next morning and beautiful she looked. The sisters had agreed to take it in turn and such a sweet smile she gave me that I was wishing I didn't have to go to work.

'God, I'm in heaven and being served by an angel,' I whispered.

'Don't let my mother hear you say that, George, or she'll have a fit,' she giggled.

'But thank you just the same. If you say the same to Mary or Nora, I'll know, and don't think they won't tell me. It'll be my turn again in three days,' she said and smiled even more sweetly as she left.

I was so taken with Ellen's pretty face that it almost slipped my mind to ask Mrs Griffin about Shanny sharing my room. I had a feeling that it would be the first thing he would ask. I picked up my tools and poked my head around the kitchen door.

'Mrs Griffin, I wondered if you might consider taking my friend, Shanny, as a lodger. I'd be prepared to share my room with him and we'd both pay the same rent. I'm afraid I did too good a job of singing your praises, and now he's desperate to come—he doesn't seem very happy where he is.'

'I'm not sure I like having my praises sung up at the airfield,

George, and I certainly wouldn't like you singing about my daughters to all your work mates either.'

I tried to look suitably hurt by the suggestion, to cover my guilt. I'd have to be a lot more careful of what I was thinking around Mrs Griffin now that she had proved she could read minds.

'Well, the money would be useful,' she said. 'But I won't have you two misbehaving. My girls are excited enough already.'

'Can I tell him yes then?'

'You can bring him home for dinner tonight and I'll see.'

'Thanks, Mrs Griffin,' I shouted, as I ran for the door.

'It's Edith, George, I don't think I like men calling me Mrs Griffin. It makes me feel old.'

Progress, I thought. 'Well goodbye, Edith. We'll see you tonight.'

Shanny was sitting at the end of the lane, waiting for me.

'Well, George? What did Mrs Griffin say? And please don't tell me you've forgotten to ask. I swear I'll cut my throat if you have, I couldn't face another fish pie.'

'Edith has invited you to dinner tonight and she'll see. So it's up to you, my boy. Behave yourself or you're out. A word of advice: keep your eyes off the girls. She doesn't miss a look and she reads minds. So if she reaches for her rolling pin, you'd better run for it. Especially keep your eyes off Ellen. She doesn't know it yet, but she's spoken for.'

I was falling over myself to stake my claim. I'd promised myself that I was finished with women, but this beauty was different. She was special.

'George, I'm talking to you,' Shanny said, poking me. 'Wake up, mate, what should I get her? You know, a little present to ease my path to heaven?'

'Women like flowers, don't they? Why don't you pick some on the airfield?'

'I don't know, George. You're sure she won't misunderstand? It might give the wrong impression, turning up with a bunch of flowers. Still, if you think so.'

I just nodded as we reached the hangar, and we set about our work.

Shanny had collected a good-sized bunch of flowers for Mrs Griffin, from heaven knows where, and when the hooter finally went, we made our way home.

'I'm going to ladle the charm on by the bucket full, my friend, until your Mrs Griffin's head spins and she's begging me to stay, George, my boy.'

'This I've got to see,' I said, my spirits returning.

We paused at the door while I inspected him. '

'Check your shoes for mud, Shanny. It wouldn't do to walk mud in Mrs Griffin's hall, or you'll be following your own footsteps back out, double quick.'

The door sprung open while we were still composing ourselves and we were confronted by Nora. She smiled a mischievous smile, first at me and then at Shanny.

'Welcome, boys. Well, George, who's your bashful friend hiding behind the flowers?'

'Shanny Francis,' I said, waving at him, 'and this is Nora,' I said, completing the introductions. Shanny seemed to have lost his tongue and just stood there open-mouthed. I nudged him and he clicked into gear.

'George told me you were a beauty, but he didn't do you justice,' he said, handing her the flowers.

'No, what I said was, that you were all beautiful,' I corrected, grabbing the flowers back, 'these belong to your mother.'

'We'll let him decide that, shall we George?' she said, grabbing them back and giving Shanny her 'you won't be sorry' look.

Shanny nodded, dribbling all down the front of his jacket.

'They are for me?' Nora squealed, 'how sweet. My, won't the others be jealous.'

She turned on her heel and walked exaggeratedly down the hall, followed by Shanny. I had a foreboding. This introduction had already gone off on a tangent and was running out of control. I could hear squealing and shouting coming from the living room and I could guess what was causing it.

I arrived, as Ellen was leaving and she gave me such a look that my words stuck in my throat. I entered the room to hear Nora relaying how we'd all but fought over her, and brought her flowers, but that she wouldn't be greedy and she would lend one or other of us to them, like any good sister would. The banter ended as Mrs Griffin came hurrying through the door.

'Which one of you has upset Ellen then? I hope it wasn't you, George.'

I shook my head and raised my eyebrows as if to signify it was none of my doing. Her eyes passed to Shanny.

'Not a very good start Mr...?'

'Francis,' Shanny chirped up, 'as in Francis of Assisi—we're both saintly.' He smiled.

'And is it you who's been bringing my Nora flowers, Mr Francis?'

I could see his banter met with her disapproval and we were on the verge of being shown the door.

'I won't have my girls upset by a couple of fancy boys, coming in here with flowers and soft words. I thought better of you, George.'

'Edith…Mrs Griffin, there's been a mistake, a misunderstanding. Shanny brought the flowers for you, didn't you, Shanny?'

He gave a slight nod, to stop me from repeating the question, and he pulled a face at me while trying to keep the truth from reaching Nora's ears.

'Mrs Griffin, it's plain to see where your girls get their good looks from," he said, in the hope of rescuing the situation, but now Nora demanded the truth.

They stood looking at us, waiting for an answer.

'Well,' I said with a smile, 'we picked the flowers to show our gratitude to all of you, and decided to hand them to the first lady we saw, that being Nora.'

Her sniff told me she hadn't swallowed my explanation, and said dinner would be in fifteen minutes.

She stalked off, not entirely satisfied, and Nora followed, suppressing a giggle and winking at the pair of us.

'Hey, George,' Shanny smiled.' Pinch me. Is this heaven or am I just dreaming?'

'It'll be a dream, if you pull a stunt like that again. You've put the cat among the pigeons. The girls don't need any excuse to squabble, so tread carefully.'

We went off to the scullery to wash up and walked into the smell of dinner that came wafting up the hall, making our mouths water.

'Now, watch your step. Don't take your eyes off the plate and we'll have no more ladling of your charm. It won't cut any ice with Edith. Mrs Griffin.'

'Well, you've managed to get on first name terms with the old Dragon so something works.'

'Some of us have got it, Shanny, and some only think they have.'

We hurried down the stairs to be confronted by a delicious rabbit pie, being served by Mary, who gave us a smile loaded with promise, as Liam used to say, in response to Nora's challenge. She was a pretty girl, and to tell the truth, there was nothing to choose between them, and I had a job to keep myself in check, never mind Shanny.

'Run along now, Mary,' Mrs Griffin said. 'And don't go listening at the keyhole.'

Mary pulled a long face but she knew better than to argue.

'Now, Mr Francis, I want to know a bit more about you. Where are you from, though I hardly need to ask from your cockney accent.'

'Whitechapel, Mrs Griffin, my mum's run a stall there all her life and I helped as soon as I could walk. I'm my dear old mum's only son, and her pride and joy. She had given up hope of having a child and then she was blessed, late on, with yours truly. She says I'm a chip off the old block, being a carpenter like my old dad. He's dead now, so there's only the two of us. She's seventy and still runs the stall in the high street. I'm twenty-four, single, interesting and virtuous, a good dancer, friendly, some might say handsome, trustworthy, honest, hard-working and altogether a very good sort.'

I was flabbergasted. What would she make of him? I had no idea, but she surprised me, she smiled. It was the first time I'd seen her smile and it changed her appearance.

The worn-out look left, and her face softened. She was an

uncommonly handsome woman when she smiled.

'That's all very well, Mr Francis, but can you cook?'

'Just give me a kitchen, Mrs G, and I'm as happy as a pig in...'

'I'll take that as a yes then. All right, you can stay on trial for a week. George knows the rules and he knows not to break them.'

I took Shanny to my room where we collapsed into each other's arms, laughing, as the door closed. This mate of mine, this cockney comic from the East End, had brought a bit of good humour into her life and the relief in her face said it was none too soon.

'I told you I'd win her over, did I not, Georgie boy?" he smiled.

'You did and I must confess I didn't believe it possible, but I'd still watch your step—you may have caught her in a good mood and what worked today may not work tomorrow.'

'Oh ye of little faith. By the time I'm finished, we'll be getting extra portions of dinner and large helpings of T.L.C. for pudding— that's tender loving care, for your information, Georgie—from the delectable Griffin girls.'

He slicked his hair down and smiled a toothy smile into the mirror, winked at himself and made for the door.

'See you downstairs. Don't be too long, I don't want you upsetting Edith. By the way George, I like to sleep on the right,' he winked.

I sighed. He was a card all right, and the first proper friend I had ever had. It was nice to have a friend. I'd had no friends of my own age. The road gang had adopted me and I was their lucky charm but that wasn't quite the same as an equal. I'd had none in Scotland either, being a tinker boy. So it was a first for me and it felt just great. I'd have to keep my past hidden just in case. Cockneys had the same prejudices as Wickers. Never again would I stand outside looking in. I renewed my promise to myself that no one down here would see the tinker boy hiding inside of me.

'George,' a voice called from the door, snapping me out of my reverie. It was a nice voice, soft and warm, and as I turned towards it, I was happy to see that it belonged to Ellen.

'Ellen,' I said as she turned to go. 'I think there has been some misunderstanding. I hope you'll let me explain, I would like us to be friends.'

'There's no need, George, I'm not upset. Nora has a way with the boys and they always fall for her. She's wicked, that's what she is, so you needn't flatter yourself that it worries me.'

I could see by her face that she was upset, and though I was sorry, I was happy that she was. It could mean that she liked me, in spite of her words.

'Well, I just wanted to say that if I'd brought any flowers for anyone, they'd most probably be for your mum.'

I could see by her face that I'd made an awful mess of my apology and that she was confused as to how to take it.

'Well, it was bad enough coming behind Nora but coming second to my mother takes the biscuit. If I'm not good enough for you to bother to bring a few measly flowers for, I don't think we can be friends.'

She flounced out, slamming the door, and opened it again to say that my tea was ready and that I was late. She liked me I could tell by the way she slammed the door in my face. I pasted on a smile and went down.

'Come on, George, I'm so hungry that they had to tie me to the chair.'

They all chuckled except Ellen, who gave me a frosty look and disappeared into the kitchen.

'You are a card, Shanny,' Mary giggled.

'Yes, the joker,' Nora added, giving him a dazzling smile.

They had a similar sense of humour, these two, and we'd have to watch out or we'd all become the butt of their jokes.

The kitchen was suddenly crowded with the arrival of Lillian, Madge and Violet, who were visiting. Add to this Laurie and Len and the three resident girls and it resembled Piccadilly Circus on a bad day, or so Shanny said. The visiting girls were expecting their husbands' home at any time, so the atmosphere was charged with excitement. Introductions were going on all around while Mrs Griffin was trying to cook dinner.

'Hands!' she shouted over her shoulder, and big as they were, they were stopped in their tracks and produced hands face up on the table. Me and Shanny followed suit. She left her oven to cast her beady eye over the array of palms. 'Over!' she said and we all obeyed.

Mrs Griffin didn't miss a trick and she pulled out one or two to go and make a better job of scrubbing their nails.

'Lillian, you've been biting your nails again. Go and get the mustard.'

Lillian looked suitably embarrassed.

'I haven't, Mum, look,' Nora said, displaying her hands for all to see.

'No, but you can wash that muck off your face before you sit at my table. Just because we have men in the house, you don't have to paint yourself up like a little tart.'

Mary and Ellen giggled behind their hands.

'When you two are perfect, you can laugh, until then keep quiet. Ellen, put another pot of potatoes on, and Len go down the garden and fetch me another cabbage. I'm supposing you'll all want feeding.'

They all nodded. She finished her rounds without comment and returned to the kitchen.

'Whew,' Laurie whistled. 'I thought I was caught,' opening his hand to show a crumpled half-smoked cigarette.

Mrs Griffin wielded supreme power in her house and I took my hat off to her. While you were under her roof you played by her rules or you didn't play at all.

'You'll have to excuse Mum,' Lillian said, for Shanny's and my benefit, taking the small pot of mustard to the table and regaining her seat. 'Dad used to have a soothing effect on her and he could tell you off and make it sound like a pat on the back.'

He must have been quite a man, this Ernest Griffin. He certainly didn't have any faults according to all present, making Mrs Griffin's loss all the harder to bear.

Nora and Mary began whispering with Violet, Madge and Lillian, no doubt telling of the debacle of the flowers and how we were her slaves. There was a lot of giggling and every now and then they'd give us a searching look and giggle again. Shanny was enjoying this attention and beamed back at them. I just felt embarrassed. Ellen came from the kitchen with a tray and could see Nora holding court. She wasn't best pleased to hear the flower story for the umpteenth time. I pushed back my chair and offered her my help, thinking I'd get the brush off, but she was to have her moment of glory.

'Thank you, George,' she said sweetly and handed me the tray.

I followed her, watched by the huddle. She gave them a haughty look as she trailed me around before them.

'Looks to me like you've got some competition,' Lillian whispered. 'If you were to ask me, I'd say its game, set and match to Ellen.'

'Well, I didn't ask you, did I?' said Nora, 'and you didn't see his face when he brought me the flowers.'

'The other one seems to be besotted with you, so be satisfied. You can't run rings around every boy you see, as much as you'd like to.'

'You always take Ellen's side, Lil. I can't help it if the boys can't resist me even your Ted gives me the eye when you're not looking.'

'What's that you're saying? My Ted wouldn't give you a second glance, you little tart.'

'Ask anyone. Ask Mary if you don't believe me, we had a good giggle about it.'

Lil spun around to confront Mary in time to see the door close. This was brewing into a major fight and Mary had slipped out before she was dragged into it. She ran straight to the kitchen to tell Ellen what she was missing. Ellen listened, snorting angrily at Nora's claims, but was soon smiling at Lil's conclusion that George was hers for the taking.

'I wish Nora hadn't said that about Ted,' Mary whispered, 'although it was probably true. He does have an eye for the ladies. He doesn't mean anything by it though, I'm sure of that, but I wouldn't want to be in his shoes when he gets home expecting love and affection,' she giggled.

'Go and find out what's happening. You can't leave it there, but don't you dare back that little hussy up, or I'll never speak to you again,' Ellen warned.

Lillian turned back, as Mary entered quietly, suppressed her rage and put on her 'London look,' as the girls knew it. The look was a haughty, superior, sophisticated look that usually put the country girls in their place.

'If you think for one moment that Ted would prefer to look at a girl when he can look at a woman, you're very much mistaken, my dear Nora.'

'Ask Mary then, if you don't believe me,' Nora said.

'I wouldn't lower myself. You two are as thick as thieves. I'll be glad to get home and away from your mucky insinuations.'

Lillian was upset. How could he give Nora the eye? She knew he loved the ladies but he was all talk. It was his naughty boy nature that made him so endearing and loveable, but that's all it was. If they took it the wrong way, then that was up to them. Nevertheless she determined to have words with him, she wouldn't be made a fool of in her own house. She gave Nora a glare and pushed by Mary out of the room. The two giggled at Lillian's ramrod back. They loved to bring her down to earth.

'Get her, with her West End look,' Nora said, prancing up and down like a model on a catwalk. She really thinks she's it, living in Fulham. Why can't she be more like you, Madge, down to earth?'

'Why can't you be more like Violet?' Madge returned. 'If you were, there'd be a lot less trouble.'

Violet had run out after Lil to apply some comfort to her elder sister.

'That downtrodden little slave, never!' Nora retorted. 'She gets what she deserves from that bullying husband of hers. If he was my husband, and he treated me the way he treats Vi, I'd make him wish he'd never been born, before I threw him out.'

'What would you do to him?' Mary whispered, smiling.

She loved to hear Nora's lurid plans for Ernie Bone, if he continued to abuse her soft, inoffensive sister. Nora put her mouth close to Mary's ear.

'I'd tie him to the bed when he was asleep and threaten to cut his balls off with his own razor, and stand them in a jar on the mantelpiece for everyone to see.'

Mary's eyes grew round as she imagined it.

'He wouldn't have dared lay a finger on her if Dad had been alive, so I'd only be doing what he would have done,' Nora said with a smile.

Lillian came into the kitchen with Vi to find Ellen. They'd always been close. Violet and Ellen weren't jealous of Lillian's move to the big city, and they admired her glamorous clothes, her sophisticated good looks, and her elegant ways. She should have been a film star with her looks, Ellen thought—she looked like Vivian Leigh with her dark black hair and pale skin. What she saw in Ted, though, Ellen couldn't imagine. Nice as he was, he was no Tyrone Power. He was kind of round in shape and bald. Vi had always imagined her with a Clark Gable, but she was happy and he doted on her, so that was fine.

'Ellen,' she whispered, pulling her away and out of her mother's earshot. 'That little bitch of a sister of ours, and I don't need to tell you which one, has been saying that my Ted has been flirting with her when my back's turned. What do you think of that? I've a good mind to tell Mum.'

'Teddy's just being Teddy,' Ellen whispered back. 'You know

what a giggle he is. We all love him, so you needn't be jealous of him.'

'He wouldn't look at another woman. He idolises you, dear,' Vi added. "Don't you know that yet? And Nora's a little jealous that you managed to escape, so don't be too hard on her.'

These comforting words took the steam out of her.

'Perhaps I should be a little more understanding. I didn't know she was eaten up with envy. It still doesn't excuse her saying what she did, though what I'd do if I were stuck in this pocket-sized village after London, I can't imagine.'

'I hope you won't say you feel sorry for Nora. It sounds a bit patronising and it'll make her worse,' Ellen said.

'Yes, better if you say nothing dear,. suggested Vi, which was always her answer to everything.

'What's all the whispering about?' Mrs Griffin asked. 'I'll tolerate no secrets in my house. You three can take some plates in and wait on the table, and send the other girls in. I have some jobs for them, and while you're at it, send Laurie out for some coal. I'm going to be late for my card game at this rate. I'd better get changed.' She left them to it and hurried upstairs. She wouldn't miss her card game for anything and they were old enough to cope. Their personal thoughts took second place now that they had tasks to perform.

We'd been listening, Shanny and me, to Len's account of his first days in the Navy.

'If I hadn't got a weekend pass, I'd have gone crazy. The only good thing about the Navy is the uniform. The girls go crazy for it. So who's going to accompany me to the dance at the village hall tonight? I'm dying to try it out,' he said, looking around.

Dinner interrupted any further discussion, and my meal disappeared in record time. It was delicious. We ate quickly while we chatted about our work and the state of the war effort, but Len was only interested in showing the girls his uniform.

'What about the dance then?' Len persisted.

The answer was cut off as the door opened and Mrs Griffin came in all dressed up and ready to go. She asked us if dinner was all right, looking at us for confirmation. I jumped in while Shanny still had his mouth full.

'Wonderful,' I said, determined to keep in her good books, and if compliments worked for him then I'd give them a try. 'What you can do with a rabbit is pure magic.'

She smiled, pleased with the compliment. I had gained another gold star to my credit and Shanny was impressed. I could tell by the way he nodded his head in agreement.

'Well,' Len said, still trying to get his group out to the dance. 'That's Ellen, me, Mary and Nora, George and Shanny. That's even numbers. Are you game, boys?'

I'd never done any dancing except at the ceilidh in Middle-thorpe and then I'd been taken in hand by big Marianne, but I had a feeling this would be altogether different and if it gave me the opportunity to hold Ellen, I was game. 'Yes,' I nodded.

'Shanny?' Len asked.

'You try and stop me,' he smiled his wide, toothy smile. 'Give us a minute while George and I make ourselves beautiful and we'll be right back. Come on, George.'

Shanny was humming happily as we climbed the stairs, and while he slicked his hair down, I tackled him.

'Before we go down, I want you to keep Nora occupied? Thanks to you Ellen's still cross about the flowers, so I've got to apply a little bit of my own magic, taught to me by Liam O'Donahue himself and never known to fail.'

'Who's this Liam O' what's-his-name then?'

'A big Irishman who's spent his life making roads, settling arguments, and making young women very happy.'

'This I've gotta see, but keeping Nora happy, that's a tough one, George. That girl's a man-eater, but I'll try because you're my mate. I only hope you'll spare me a thought, when she's making a meal of me,' he smiled.

'I'll say grace for you: For what she is about to receive may the Lord make her truly thankful, how will that do?'

We were still laughing as we came down the stairs.

'Ellen's not coming, boys,' Len said. 'She promised Mum she'd clear up, and then sit in with Laurie and Evie, so that leaves five.'

'Change of plan,' I whispered in Shanny's ear. 'I'll stay behind and help,' I said.

She looked over a pile of plates with an impish look in her eye.

'That leaves four. We'd better go, or at this rate I'll be going on my own,' Len said.

I grabbed some plates as they put on their coats. Len pushed his hat at a jaunty angle as Madge came through the door.

'Very saucy Len, all the good girls love a sailor, isn't that how it goes?'

'I sincerely hope not, Madge. Good girls weren't exactly what I had in mind, if we ever get there, that is.'

'Sorry, Ellen dear,' Madge said. 'You get off. I said I'd look after

Laurie and Evie for you and I will. Go on, I'll finish the clearing up.'

'George has gallantly offered to stay and help, haven't you, George?' Ellen said, smiling sweetly.

She'd been luring me like my Dada lured the trout, and I was landed and stranded.

'Yes, of course, I would, but then you'd have an odd number so…' I left it hanging.

'No need, you sweet man,' Madge said. 'Ellen told me you were taking her to the dance, so I'll manage, you get off.'

Ellen had had her revenge, and I had slipped skilfully out of the trap. Liam would be proud of me.

'Oh well, it looks like it's me and you, Shanny,' Nora said, grabbing his arm and dragging him clear of Mary.

'You said we'd share them, you rotten little pig,' Mary moaned.

'You can have him, when I'm finished,' Nora said, squeezing him tighter. 'Though there might not be much left.'

Mary looked from Ellen to George for a ray of hope, but you couldn't see daylight between them.

'It's you and me then Len, and don't go dropping me for the first girl to flash her frillies at you.'

We arrived at the dance-hall door and found it throbbing with American servicemen from the camp and a small but impressive band playing a popular dance tune. Ellen was whisked away from right under my nose, and out on to the floor by some Yank, and they were soon swallowed up by the rapidly filling dance floor. Thoughts of Middle-Thorpe came flowing back only this time I was a local trying to hang onto his girl, and the Yanks were playing the part of the road gang.

I could see now how these meetings inevitably ended in a free-for-all and this one was definitely heading in that direction.

'It didn't take you long to lose your girl George,' Shanny smiled. 'What would your big Irishman have done about that?' he chuckled.

'He'd go get her back, just like I'm going to.' As I ploughed through the crowd I heard Shanny's warning following me, 'Steady George, don't be too hasty.'

I found them just in front of the band and I tapped him on the shoulder.

'Excuse me,' I said politely, Liam had always taught me to try to find a civilized solution, before you decked them.

'Get lost Shorty,' he drawled, giving me a snarl.

I tapped him again.

'I think you've mistakenly walked off with someone that belongs to me, and I'd appreciate her return.'

'Listen Shorty, I'll tell you one more time, go look somewhere else before I get cross.'

The crowd seemed to sense the trouble and somehow cleared the space around us.

I could see Ellen struggling to get out of his grasp.

'Calm down George, we don't want any trouble,' Ellen pleaded.

He should have let her go, and he may have stood a chance of avoiding the haymaker that floored him. I think everyone in the place heard his nose break in the silence that followed. The band struck up in an effort to restore order but we were way past such remedies. All hell broke loose as his mates piled in. I took a few punches and got a few away before the cavalry arrived and started to tear bodies off me.

Liam and John-Joe were beside me in spirit, though as I scrapped I wished it had been in body. Order was restored eventually as we all ran out of wind and I staggered back to where the girls were waiting.

'A real spectacle you made of yourself George. Whatever came over you?' Ellen said brushing me down.

'Well I think you were wonderful Georgie. Take no notice of her, ungrateful little bitch,' Nora chirped up, 'fancy, having the whole American base slugging it out with the locals over you.'

Her eyes came alive, sparkling at the thought.

'Shanny would you do the same for me?'

He nodded as she bathed his swollen eye, 'but just don't ask me to prove it too soon.'

'Sit down George while I fix your face. Look at you, your suit's ruined and your shirt's torn, but I have to say I'm proud of you,' she whispered, looking around at the audience That had gathered.

Len had found an admirer to mop his brow and was going through the fight blow by blow.

'All right, George?' Shanny asked, coming up behind me as the girls went to powder their noses. 'I tell you boy that was some fight—England one: Yanks zero. But a word in your ear, no not that one, it looks like someone tried to tear it off. He shuffled around to the other side. That Nora is going to wear me out. She fits me like a second skin. Tell me something, George, have I got a ring through my nose?'

'What? A ring, did you say?'

'Yes, a ring, with a lead attached?'

'No, of course you haven't. What on earth are you babbling on about?'

'Well, I could swear that whenever she tugs, I follow—whether I want to or not.' He shook his head in disbelief. 'George, I'm not sure Nora's going to let me behave myself and I have to admit this is a new one on me. That girl's got me bamboozled, like a lamb to the slaughter, and I love it.'

'Well, you'd better behave. I don't want you ruining my relationship with Edith...that's Mrs Griffin to you. Remember, these girls tell each other everything, so if you let her have her way with you, by tomorrow they'll all know, and before long so will Mrs Griffin.'

'Well, what am I going to say? She's already gone for her coat.'

'Tell her the forbidden fruit tastes that much sweeter when it's left on the tree a little longer.'

'Brilliant! But that's the sort of thing the local virgin might say to me! I couldn't possibly tell her that! I'd become a laughing stock and the girls would avoid me like the plague. Anyway where did you get that one from? It sounds like a passage from The Virgin's Guide to Martyrdom.'

'All I'm saying is, it'll buy you a little time. Stick close to me, and don't let her get you on your own.'

'I can't believe we're saying this, George. Perhaps I'd better just give in. After all, they may drop a bomb on the Aerodrome tomorrow and my dying memory will be of my last fight to preserve my good name and of Nora having to go through life without me.'

'So be it,' I said as the girls came back.

I grabbed Ellen and made for the dance floor. We waltzed around and at last I could hold her close and it felt good. I was still getting some looks from the Yanks but they'd pulled their horns in and were giving us a lot more respect.

When the music ended we wandered back.

Shanny was giving Nora a twirl. She giggled, giving him the eye.

'Are you ready for home yet, Shanny boy?'

I saw him look over at me but I was busy, so against my better judgment, he gave himself up without a fight and left.

We left soon after and as we passed the Yanks, the big guy was nursing his nose and his once smart uniform looked a mess. Liam had taught me never to hold a grudge, so I said a polite 'Goodnight.' They didn't know what to make of it so they just scowled.

'I'm sorry, George. It was my fault. I was only trying to make you a bit keener,' Ellen said. 'I should have refused him, but I messed it up and you and Shanny got hurt. Nora's right, I'm a bitch and I don't deserve you. Where on earth did you learn to fight like that?' she giggled.

I was tempted to blurt out the secret of my background and take a chance on her taking me for what I was. I was sure she would, but not so sure about her mum.

I dare not, so I didn't.

Some-day I would share the good things about tinker life, as well as the bad, and we'd laugh together. I just said that she was worth fighting for, and that her partner wouldn't be as handsome in the morning with his flattened nose. She pulled me to her and kissed me softly.

We stood at her gate for what seemed like five minutes but was probably much more, when a voice said, 'Hello, hello, what's going on here?'

I jumped out of my skin. I think Ellen had dropped off in my arms because she woke with a start and gave Shanny a warm smile.

'I should take the warmth out of your smile. Your mum's coming up the lane and she's sure to guess what that smile means.'

Ellen sprung up the path and let herself in as Mrs Griffin came around the bend.

'What are you two waiting for Christmas?'

'For you, dear lady,' Shanny said. 'We've been here all night, isn't that right, George?'

I nodded, trying to avoid her scrutiny.

'Just cooling off you might say, Mrs G...Edith,' I said, which was as near the truth as she was going to get.

'You've been up to no good by the look of you.'

We gave her an 'innocence personified' look that would have fooled most people but not Mrs Griffin.

'I've already heard so don't go to the trouble of lying to me. I hope you gave those Yanks a good hiding they're too cocky by half. You're sure you're not Irish, George?' she said. 'My Ernest was part Irish and he had that Celtic charm and the strength of a horse to go with it, bless him.'

'No, I'm not Irish, but I've been taught by someone who is,' I answered, and she smiled and left. We followed her in and I pushed Shanny up the stairs before the light could expose his face. It was covered in lipstick and it was my guess Mrs Griffin would know exactly where it had come from. In the room I pushed him in front of the mirror.

'Look at the state of you. So much for letting the forbidden fruit, hang on the tree.'

'That girl knows more ways to make you do the things you want to do, but know you shouldn't,' he smiled. 'Life's too short, George, to waste time with your 'gently gently catchy monkey' approach. That girl had a queue forming behind me, which stretched back half a mile, and now the War's underway who knows where we'll be, or what'll become of us, so we'd better fill our spare time with pleasure while we can. I lifted that little gem straight from none other than Mrs G herself.'

We both went to sleep that night with lopsided smiles pasted firmly on our swollen faces, and a sorry pair we must have looked, battered and bruised. But I was sure Liam, my Dada, Jonno and Charlie would all have been proud of me.

There was a lot of activity around the Aerodrome, bigwigs from the Air force were being shown around by Mr MacCloud, and they were studying a blueprint. Mr MacCloud called us all to gather round and introduced us to an air vice-marshal, who explained how vitally important our work was, and that he needed our best efforts if we were to defeat the Nazis.

'Our planes will be our saviour, so we'll need to produce a constant supply. Our top brains have come up with a new design, which we hope will be superior to anything the Hun has, and you're the men who will take this piece of paper and make it fly.'

Although I knew that this little speech meant more work and longer hours, I wouldn't complain, I was thankful for the good food, good company and comparative safety, I worked together with Shanny on the new project—it was designed to be the fastest, most manoeuvrable, fighter in existence and it had to be strong but light. We worked night and day to get it right, and it was tested and tinkered with until it was perfect—and then, and only then, would it finally go into construction. Nobody could say where it would be built, we had no idea. My fear was that it would be moved, along with the workforce, to some other part of the country and I would have to leave Norfolk.

I was in fear of moving on. I could only reason that I'd lost my family once, and now, just as this substitute family appeared, I may have to move on again. I had a need and they were fulfilling it.

We worked longer and harder for the next few weeks and I saw little of my bed and less of Ellen. She was now working as housekeeper to the local vicar, cooking and cleaning and only coming home to sleep. I'd convinced myself that someone was conspiring to keep us apart, so I made it my nightly duty to meet her from work and walk her home. Our relationship had blossomed and on the nightly walks home from the vicarage we talked of our hopes for the future and I was pleased that we both wanted the same things, and for my part the sooner the better.

We were, I admit it, in love, but in those confusing and insecure days, where all-out war seemed inevitable, all personal wishes were meant to take second place. But if that was what was required, then I for one wanted no part of it. The desire to have what you could today and bugger tomorrow seemed to me much more important. It was this feeling of fragility that pushed me into my proposal of marriage and prompted Ellen to accept.

We felt awkward being so happy with so much doom and gloom in the newspapers, but selfishly we wrapped ourselves in a bubble and locked out the world. I knew, of course, that my proposal was just that—an idea—a product of wishful thinking, a temporary relief to raise the spirits, no more.

Any day our bubble could burst. I was in no position to support a wife and that's how Mrs Griffin would see it, so a secret it must stay, though it was nice to know that my beautiful Ellen felt the same way. It was the beginning of the best and the worst year of my life.

We were entering a hostile, chaotic period, where decisions about our lives were taken daily by the authorities, who showed scant regard for personal circumstances. Yet because of Ellen, it was also the happiest.

Shanny and I sat in Ellen's front parlour with the whole family grouped around a crackling radio, and listened to Mr Chamberlain tell us we were officially at war. This was not welcome news to Ellen and me, or anyone else, I dare say, but I could only think of what it meant to us. From the moment of the broadcast, the lives of the whole population would be changed. Would Jonno, Charlie and Hughie join up, or abscond as their elders had in the Great War?

Within weeks the whole country was on the move, rumours were circulating at the Aerodrome that the whole Hurricane operation might soon be moved to London, and there were posters everywhere warning about careless talk costing lives. I tried to ignore the consequences of a move, but I couldn't.

'George,' Ellen said as we walked home from the vicarage on a quiet and peaceful night, 'let's get married before this damned war can separate us.'

She said it with such determination that I could only nod my head and promise to approach her mother as soon as we reached home. I knew it was coming, and I knew there was no way to avoid it. I'd carried my birth certificate folded neatly in my wallet and that small piece of paper told the story of my birth at the Latheron workhouse and it carried my father's mark in the form of an X. It listed his tinker lifestyle and there, for all to see, my mother and father bearing the same name. What would Ellen make of it? What would her mother make of it? My secret was about to surface and I could lose everything. I pulled Ellen to a stop and faced her, not knowing how to begin.

'I have to tell you something.'

The apprehension showing in Ellen's eyes said that I'd started badly.

'What is it, George? What's wrong?'

I opened my wallet and handed her my birth certificate. It was all there in black and white for her to see and it would say it clearer than I could. She read it slowly, looking up at me every time a new fact registered. She said nothing. She folded it slowly and handed it back. I placed it back into my wallet and cursed myself for having created a make-believe life. I felt I'd tricked my way into her heart by pretending to be something I wasn't.

We walked on in silence, while Ellen's mind scurried like a frightened mouse, looking for what I expected to be a way out. I could stand this silence no longer.

'Look, Ellen, I'm so sorry. I should have told you, but I thought I could run away from my roots. I should have known better.'

'George, my own sweet father's family were Irish tinkers, he told me so himself, though you'd never hear it from my mother. My grandfather ran off with a landowner's daughter who was disinherited by her family, at least that's the story. My dad was an honest man and he'd never pretend to be what he's not and that's what I loved most about him. I'm disappointed in you, George. You couldn't find a sweeter man in this world than my dad and I don't give a fig where he came from.'

She'd gone cold and I could see that I'd been exposed as a bigger snob than the townies I'd run away from. I didn't know quite where that left me and Ellen. A minute ago we were talking of getting married and now? Who knows? She unexpectedly started to put my confession into perspective.

'Of course, you shouldn't tell Mum, not straight away. She's a bit proper and she doesn't hold with tinkers. She thinks everyone should know their place and be respectable, but no more hiding your past. If you're asked, you'd better tell the truth. God forbid that your family should ever know of your denial, George. Tell me about them and tell it as it is.'

For the first time, I spoke openly about the hardships and the prejudice that had warped my mind, of my wish to stay at school, and of Angus and Aggie, of Jonno, Charlie, Jeannie and Hughie, of my earliest recollections of the travelling life, and of the stories told to me of our clan, but most of all my Dada's sacrifice in staying put to give us a new life. It wasn't of his choosing but my mother had promised on my life to put us first and I will always be grateful to her for her strength.

I'd left out the reason I had to leave in such a hurry, knowing that although I was stripping myself bare, the Maggie Crook part would be suicide.

'I hope I love my children enough to let them go, the way your parents did,' she said.

I'd been made to see the shallowness of my feelings, shamed by my denial of Mother and Dada, whose only crime was to be born tinkers.

Ellen understood how the prejudice had shaped my young life and she understood why I had buried my family.

'You desperately wanted to be thought of as respectable, without the burden of prejudice to bring you down, to be given an equal start, and your parents would be proud that you've achieved it.'

For the first time in England I could think of myself as Geordie and it lifted a great burden from me.

I decided to ask Ellen's mother for her permission to marry that very night, and so we hurried home, knowing that, whatever the obstacles, we would be together from this moment on and for the rest of our lives. We arrived home and the moment I touched the door handle, doubt crept into my mind. I still harboured feelings of inferiority, which more often than not would send me on to the attack. This I knew would not be the right course of action, if I was trying to win her mother's approval, but in these circumstances I had no control over my own feelings. My natural defence mechanism was such that it would burst forth unannounced and out of control.

It was in this state of readiness for battle that I entered the arena of her home, and leaving Ellen to wait, I burst straight into the kitchen. Unfortunately, it was bad timing and a bad place for delicate matters of the heart. Mrs Griffin was upset, about what I had no idea, but she was in no mood for my declaration of love for her favourite daughter, never mind that I wanted to marry her. But I had the steam up and without much subtlety, gave her chapter and verse of our intentions, whilst she was clearly grappling with her own problems. 'Out of the question, George,' she waved me away, as if I were a child asking for the moon. I didn't move, so she turned, placed her hands on her hips and gave me both barrels.

'Although I hate to say it George, the truth of the matter is, you're just not good enough for my Ellen.'

I was shoved back on my heels and could think of no sensible reply, except to say that I loved her and she loved me, and as far as we were concerned, that was what really mattered.

'That's complete drivel, George. You've been reading too many books. If my girls are to escape the hardships that I've had, they must marry well. I'm sorry, George, but I think you should leave and forget all about Ellen. You'll find someone else, a good looking boy like you.'

Ellen must have been listening at the door, because she came bursting in We both stared in her direction. The usually sweet, mild-mannered girl was bristling with indignation.

'Mother, how could you say such things about George? I love him, as you loved my dad, and I don't imagine your Ernest came with a dowry but that didn't stop you, thank goodness, and you couldn't have chosen a sweeter man.'

'Life was different then, Ellen. We were brought up to expect hardships, we knew nothing else, but you have the chance to better yourself. A girl as pretty as you are, and who can cook as good as any chef, will be a great catch for any man. It would be foolish to marry the first man you meet. No, I'm sorry, I won't allow it and that's my final word on the subject.'

This was developing into a major rift. I hadn't meant to come between mother and daughter, but seeing Ellen fighting for us swelled my heart with pride and made me more determined than ever to stand firm.

'Look,' I said, but before I could utter another word, Mrs Griffin, slammed her rolling pin on the table and stopped me in my tracks.

'That's my final word on the subject. There'll be no blessing from me and I know George wouldn't steal you away like a thief in the night without my approval,' she said tapping her rolling pin threateningly. I'd never known her wrong before but if she believed that that was the end of the matter then she had a surprise coming. As I opened my mouth Ellen cut me off and spun to face her mother.

'What about our baby then?' she said, tossing her head.

'What was that? Baby, whose baby? You're never expecting his child, you wicked girl.'

Mrs Griffin turned on me with her rolling pin and if I hadn't darted out of the door she would have hospitalised me for sure.

I retreated to the gate. My head was in a spin and visions of Maggie Crook came flooding back. It seemed that I was destined to be a father, real or imaginary, at least in the eyes of the world. My past was coming back to haunt me, but this time I wasn't going to run away from it. I strode back into the kitchen and found them both crying.

'Alright, I'll leave. But I'll be back, and if Ellen still wants me, I'll find us a place and we'll be married with or without your consent, Edith…Mrs Griffin.'

I left without another word and went to my room.

Shanny was dozing as I started to pack. I couldn't go that night, but I'd take my clothes with me in the morning and find somewhere.

'What's up, George?' Shanny asked, half asleep.

'I'm leaving and Ellen'll be joining me as soon as I find a suitable place for us. We'll be getting married and you'll be my Best Man. I think that about covers it. Oh, and Mrs Griffin doesn't approve,' I said, snapping my bag shut.

'Isn't this all a bit sudden, George? I mean, you can't leave me at the mercy of Mrs G, especially if you're going to steal her favourite daughter away. Sit down and let old Shanny find a way out. If there's one thing I'm good at, George, it's extracting myself from life's manure heaps. I've learned never to be too hasty. Tell me first what she said, and you needn't bother to tell me what you said, I can guess.'

'She said I wasn't good enough for her daughter and that she could do much better for herself, so I should leave and forget her.'

'Yes,' Shanny said.

'What do you mean…'Yes'?' I said.

'I mean, what did you expect? What mother thinks that there are any men good enough for their daughters? If I remember rightly, she didn't think very much of Ted, but it didn't stop Lillian from running off with him.'

'You're right Shanny, they don't come any better than me. I'm short, dark and handsome, good in a fight and against that I've got no prospects, no money and nowhere to live.'

'Umm, not good George, I must admit. We'll have to boost the good list a bit. Have you got a rich father tucked away anywhere?'

I shook my head.

'What does he do, your dad?'

'He's a trader,' I said warily.

'That's good George, a businessman, like my mother. We can make the most of that.'

Dada had been called many things, but a businessman wasn't one of them. No, I couldn't lie about that. Ellen knew the truth and wouldn't stand for it.

'No Shanny, I won't trade off my fathers' name.'

'Well then,' he thought for a minute, 'how about kind, considerate, and polite? The Yanks can vouch for that. It might be enough to sway her.'

It had been a shock for Mrs Griffin to hear my proposal out of the blue, she had no reason to think we were that serious, and if it hadn't been for the war adding a recklessness to our life plan, we would have taken things at a gentler pace. There was no time for long courtships now. I could be moved at the drop of a hat and I had to have Ellen with me. All I had to do was convince her mother that that's what we both wanted.

I immersed myself in my work and thought as little as possible about my personal problems. I hadn't spoken to Ellen since the confrontation and I had only the briefest conversation with Mrs Griffin, who said that I could stay but that I was to keep myself to myself. She wasn't one to cut off her nose to spite her face, and the loss of my money would have been a blow she could do without. Each night I was quick to eat my tea and to vanish to my room.

I would have given anything to know what had gone on between mother and daughter, and I cursed myself for walking out. I had chosen the wrong option and was now destined never to know the outcome of their fight or who had had their way.

The saga of the non-existent baby seemed to trigger a domestic maelstrom and by the look in their eyes, I could tell that everybody in residence and probably half the cronies at the whist drive were following events with the greatest interest. I could imagine my name being whispered as the villain of the piece and my being tried and found guilty of stealing a village maid's virginity, under the very nose of her family.

Liam would laugh at this kind of gossip. He'd say, 'It'll make you all the more desirable to the fairer sex, Georgie.'

Thank God that Shanny was on my side. He fed me information that he picked up from the girls. Only Shanny and Evie had any time for me—Shanny because he was a mate, and Evie because, bless her, she didn't know any better. Otherwise I was left to myself.

I spent Sunday in my room, reading and trying to make sense of things. I searched high and low for my diary. Perhaps it would show me where I'd gone wrong.

I thought back to my first encounter with Maggie Crook, which had left me penniless and with a huge feeling of guilt. Jonno had seen and enjoyed her favours without a backward glance, but not me, I had to make more of it than it was. Then there was Isabel. I had been drunk, it's true, but she'd made a fool of me so easily and I'd learned nothing from any of this. I had been much younger then, a boy, in the hands of scheming females. Now I was a man armed with the Irishman's Guide to Successful Courtship and I'd watched a master at work.

What would Liam have done I wondered? He wouldn't skulk in his room and become the invisible man. No, if they want to fight over me, he'd say then I must show them that I'm worth it. I had two choices: to leave and run away, or stand and be counted. I'd run away from the trouble at home, but that was the last time I'd run. I'd lost my family and buried my roots because of it. This time I made up my mind to face the wrath and have the woman I wanted, whatever. My diary, I suspected, was still languishing in Liam's new safe, so I would have to stop looking back to what had been said and done, and move on.

With that I got up and went down to face them. Shanny was there having a drink, while the women, I was quickly informed, were at church.

'They're praying, Georgie boy, led by the high priestess herself,' he giggled, 'for your imminent departure for foreign parts,' he added, raising his glass in a salute to the empty kitchen. 'You, my boy, have committed a cardinal sin, in trying to make off with the crown jewels. Have a little snifter and join the naughty boy brigade. I've had a good bollocking this morning for not going to church, and all I said was that we had something very important to finish.' With that he raised the half-empty bottle and gave it a big kiss.

We got thoroughly drunk and giggled at my misfortune. I suggested that it might be a good idea to disappear before the women got home, seeing as I was already in enough trouble without adding more fuel to an already blazing fire. He agreed that discretion was most definitely the better part of valour, and with that piece of wisdom we left. I, at least, had one ally in the house. This was reassuring, but did nothing to solve my problem. I was persuaded to take a leaf out of Shanny's book and ride the storm until another crisis appeared to take my place in the minds of the women.

The crisis I was looking for appeared, as if by magic, on Monday morning, plastered across the front pages of the daily papers. The news that ration books were being distributed to deal with the shortages of all sorts of food and clothing was greeted with dismay. Add to this the call for women to join the workforce to boost production for the war effort and it seemed the war had come into our homes and involved everyone. The civilian population was being relegated to second place, and that was something we'd just have to get used to. The boys had been summoned back to their units post haste, and suddenly all our minds were focused on whatever was about to come. Everything else was forgotten.

I saw Ellen that evening, knowing it would be the last time we would meet for several weeks. Our work duties had been posted on the news board at the Aerodrome and they left little time for anything but sleep. On the odd occasion that I'd meet Ellen from work and walk her home, I'd feel strange in her company. So I decided enough was enough.

'Ellen,' I said pulling her round to face me.' Will you marry me, yes or no?'

'You know I will, but it can't be now, George. This damned war has taken priority over everything, whether we like it or not. Mum's sending me and Nora to London to work in service, to make way for more boarders. She says the people from the Grange asked her about us, for their friends in Kent. They say all their staff have been called up and they're desperate for girls to live in.'

I was speechless. Mrs Griffin had had her way, of that I was sure. I knew this enforced separation could be the end for us and so, I suspect, did she.

'I'll write, George, I promise I will, so don't you forget your pledge. You won't, will you?' she said, prodding me. 'I love you,

George, but I have to think about my family. They need the money. I'll come back and when I do we'll be married, whatever they say.'

She hugged me and ran off, leaving me empty but filling with anger—at the war, at her mother, even at Ellen herself. Mrs Griffin had given Ellen the chance to see what lay out there in this crazy world and I had to face the truth that I might never see her again.

The next few months went by without much humour.

'All work and no play, makes Jack a very dull boy, George,' Shanny would say, in an attempt to drag me out of my gloom. He was soon over Nora and he tried to help me, but I would have none of it.

Ellen wrote to me religiously once a week, telling me of her life and work at Holbrook House. She said the family she worked for were very nice, and that they had two sons away fighting in France. They had only needed one of the girls and they had taken Ellen because she could cook. Nora had landed in the house of a gold coaster two streets down and was being chased, from morning to night, by the dirty old bugger.

Gold coasters are plantation owners, George,' wrote Ellen, 'who are used to chasing and catching poor little negro house servants. Nora dare not report it to the lady of the house or she wouldn't get a reference, but she got her own back before she left—she spat in his soup and watched while he finished every last bit. Good for her, I say. I'm glad it wasn't me. There's nothing much to do here, so we visit Lil on our day off and go for cycle rides.' She added as a p.s. that she was thinking of me and hoped I was behaving myself, and signed it lots of love, Ellen.'

I replied to her letters and tried to sound casual about our separation. I said they'd been working me so hard that I didn't have the time or the energy to misbehave, plus her mother was still gunning for me and I was convinced she'd got spies everywhere. We were working night and day now. Shanny was on nights, and I was on days for one week, and then we'd swap, so I saw less of him. When we were on days we were also on call at night for fire duty. We were told that there was an ever increasing risk of attack from German bombers, who were constantly on the look-out to destroy or slow down our aircraft production, so we learned to sleep lightly.

§

Robert McPhee

Chapter Eight

Goodbye Shanny

It was on just such a night that I woke from a light sleep, a sixth sense, call it what you will. I looked at the clock. It was 2am.

The steady drone that woke me was out of place. I went to the window, pulling back the blind. I'd never heard bombers in formation, but I instantly knew that was what I was hearing now. I threw my clothes on and dashed from the house. I had an ominous feeling, where was the siren warning? I knew the noise inside the aerodrome would drown the sound of the bombers, but they had people on watch duty didn't they? I knew that they were prone to doze off through boredom, watching empty skies night after night. I just prayed that they hadn't dozed off tonight.

I was full of panic as I raced up the road, shouting at the top of my voice. Suddenly the siren blast came, followed within a minute by the first bomb. It ripped into the hangar like a ball of fire. Suddenly lights flooded the sky above, and anti-aircraft guns opened up. They were no match for the planes and could only offer token resistance as the bombs rained down, destroying hangar after hangar. I reached the perimeter fence and found the gate locked in a pathetic attempt to keep the danger out. I climbed it and raced to meet the men flooding out, some injured and bleeding.

I knew them all—I'd leave them to those coming after me. I could hear the bells of our fire appliance now as it raced to the worst fires. I ignored them too and made for our workplace. It had been hit and was badly damaged. The smouldering bodies of my workmates lay all around. Mr MacCloud lay on his back looking up through the roof of the damaged hangar and as I reached him, he opened his eyes.

'Ahh Georgie McPhee, there ye are. Get back ti yer work yer highland tinker,' he whispered before he died.

He was the first man I'd ever seen die, I was in shock as I jumped up, shouting for

Shanny. I could see in the shadowy light our work place, and Shanny's body draped across our bench. He'd been hit by flying debris, but looked peaceful as if he was lying asleep in our bed. I stood for a long time, too numb to move, too shocked to cry. I finally bent and picked him up and carried him toward the exit. The all-clear was being sounded as I reached the door. I took him out onto the grass where I gently laid him down. My legs gave way and I fell down beside him and shut my eyes, as I had once before, in an effort to blot out the reality.

I tried to wipe away the image, and believe I would wake up with everything restored to normal. I lay there talking to Shanny and admonishing him for sleeping on the job, and saying that Mrs G wanted us home for dinner—our rabbit pie would be getting cold, and she would accept no excuses. I opened my eyes and stared at the pale still body. The life, the spirit, the humour had all drained away like water emptying from a sink, leaving a shell that didn't look like the man I remembered. His words at the dance came back to me, I had insisted that he ignore Nora and save himself for another day.

'George, perhaps I'd better just give in. After all, they may drop a bomb on the Aerodrome tomorrow and my dying memory will be of my last fight to preserve my good name, and of Nora having to go through life without me.'

I was so glad he took no notice of me that night.

'Shanny,' I said, 'you were right and I was so wrong.'

This moment would change me, as it had changed my Dada, in the Great War.

I stood and took a deep breath and the sounds of confusion came to me like someone turning up the volume. I looked to see people from the village tending to the wounded or searching for faces they knew, and my eyes locked onto Edith, making her way toward me, grey in the early morning light. She burst into tears at the sight of Shanny and collapsed in my arms. I'd never seen her like this, sobbing as she would for her own son.

Ellen and Nora came racing home, with the news of the many casualties they had read about in the papers weighing on their mind. They ran up the lane toward home, tears flooding down their faces and prayers on their lips. Into the parlour they came like a storm, looking fearfully from mother, to Vi and on to Mary. I came into the room to find a silence disturbed only by tears. 'George, you're safe,' Ellen squealed, running to my arms. I was looking over her shoulder at Nora's face as she watched the door for Shanny to come. Her eyes swivelled to meet mine and I shook my head sadly. I left them to their crying and walked outside and up the lane. Dada had once said that war was full of tragedy 'but ye must pull yer cap down tight and walk on or wither in grief.' I pulled my shoulders back and went into the house.

The mass funeral in the village was a sombre affair and I stood with Ellen on one side, and Nora on the other, both weeping for the cockney lad we all loved. I was glad when it was over. Shanny's mother was there but I could say very little to her, though she knew all about me and the girls from his letters home. She said she was grateful that he had been among friends when his time had come. Shanny would have been proud of the dignity she showed, in the face of such terrible waste.

Nora decided to return to London and fill Ellen's position, and get on with her life, but the sparkle was gone, extinguished by a German bomb.

Later, when Ellen and I were alone, we said a lot of personal things, which confirmed that our feelings were even greater since our separation, and I asked her again if she would marry me. She nodded that she would, with or without her mother's blessing. We resolved to go to the registry office as soon as we could find a place. I was galvanised into action and searched the newspapers for rooms or a small flat as near to the Aerodrome as possible. It had been severely damaged and our job now was to rescue what we could, and transfer it to the DeHavilland factory near London as soon as possible. The next few weeks went in a blur. When I wasn't working, I was home-hunting, and just as I was about to give up, I found a bed-sitting room with a small kitchenette screened by a curtain. It had all the essentials: an oven, sink and one small cupboard.

The rent was one pound per week, not including the gas and electricity. I was very pleased with my find and it was within walking distance of the Aerodrome. The young couple who had occupied it before us had been posted, and that had been my good luck. I couldn't wait to show Ellen how resourceful I could be if I set my mind to it, so, with the smile pasted securely back on my face, I set off to meet her from work. What would my mother think of me now? A lot had happened since I left Wick, and just now I felt further removed from my roots than ever. This new George, who was about to be married, would hardly be recognisable to anyone at home, and as my life continued to develop, I had the feeling that I would become further estranged. On August 1st 1939 we were married without the presence of Mrs Griffin, and with just Vi to vouch for us. This would have been unthinkable in peace time, and it hurt me to deny Ellen the day she deserved, but, in this climate, couples were marrying in haste before being dragged apart by this awful war. Ellen remained positive that her family would come round and all would be forgotten in the confusion of the war. The truth soon came out about the so-called baby and her mother gave me her version of an apology.

'Well George, baby or no baby, my opinion remains the same, although you're not as big a villain as some say.'

Whether all her cronies would be treated to the truth I had my doubts, my character was now tarnished and that wouldn't be forgotten. Ellen insisted that we were two halves of the same coin, in an effort to gain her mother's support, but she wasn't going to back down easily.

'Ellen has made her bed so now she must lie in it,' she said.

And lie in it we did. My passionate nature soon got the better of me, and before long Ellen fell pregnant. I was reminded of my own workhouse birth and my mother's determination to sacrifice the family's freedom for me. I truly understood that feeling for the first time when I held Stewart.

Mrs Griffin did eventually come round, with Violet's help, and was always looking after our baby, as well as Lillian's toddler and Violet's two girls. Ellen was as happy as a mother hen with all her sisters and their children around her while the men were away in their own private hell.

The war was going badly for our fleet. Both Navy and merchant shipping were both being sunk at will, which worried us all, knowing Len was aboard ship somewhere in the war zone. Information was scarce all we had, was hope to sustain us and the news to scare us. According to the newspapers it was only the Air force that was on a par with the German war machine, which, of course, meant we had to get back into full operation. Rumours circulated every now and then about when we would be moving to the bigger site, near London. This news was worrying, but we realised that we all had to make sacrifices if we were going to get through this. My thoughts turned once again to home and my Dada's miraculous survival from the trenches of the Great War and my mother's struggle to feed us in the years he was away.

I read the notice board as I did every day on arrival, hoping I wouldn't see my name. My heart sank as it was there at the top of the list. I'd been posted along with the team building Spitfires to the DeHavilland factory near London with immediate effect. I had just the weekend to break the news to Ellen before being transported first thing on Monday morning, so I'd have to leave right away. I hurried home, not knowing how she'd take the news and in true Geordie fashion I blurted it out.

'Ellen, sit down, I have some news,' I said.

'George you do pick your times. I've got to see to the baby, he wants feeding.'

I think she knew what was coming and didn't want to hear it. I came out with it in a rush.

'I've been posted,' I said. 'We can move you and the baby back to your mother's, tomorrow.'

'You mean we've been posted, don't you? From what the girls say families are allowed to move with their husbands so we'd better get cracking.

'Ellen was determined to follow me and wouldn't listen to her mother and stay in the relatively bomb-free area, surrounded by her family, not even for the baby's sake.

'We vowed for better or worse to stay together,' and I'm not letting you out of my sight again, so I'll hear no more about it."

And that's how we came to the big city

§

Chapter Nine

London in Flames

Although it was war time and things were uncertain, nothing could calm the feeling of excitement we got from being so near London. Everything seemed so big: the shops, the buildings and with people everywhere. It was like God had disturbed a nest of ants with a big stick and they were swarming back and forth with no obvious purpose. We were country people and unused to the crowds. Servicemen were everywhere young boys, younger than me, all dressed up and ready to go. I felt embarrassed that I had been excused national service, and had to join the old and infirm in the home guard.

I had my Dada's pride and would have marched away gladly if I had been given the chance.

We were billeted with Lucy Simpkin, a fearsome lady with a little girl a bit older than Stewart, and with a husband away in the Air force. She epitomised the bulldog spirit we'd been hearing about and it was catching. Ellen and Lucy became great friends and that helped me in the long hours of factory work and my nightly sessions with the fire crew. It was hard, dangerous work and though tired from the factory, I was glad to take some risks for my pride's sake.

We'd get to go out on the odd day I had off, and Lucy would baby-sit. We'd go to the pictures and stand in a queue that would often stretch down the street and around the corner, servicemen with their girls, soldiers, sailors, and airmen, all wanting a little relief from the reality of war.

Programme sellers, buskers, even acrobats would keep us entertained during the wait for the cinema to open its doors. We'd listen to the banter of the crowd and the newest jokes about Hitler that made us laugh, and treat ourselves to some hot chestnuts roasted on a grill set up on the pavement, and smelling like heaven. The heaving crowd propelled us forward as the doors opened, and down the aisle to the sixpenny stalls we'd swarm. This warm, dark theatre with its crystal chandeliers and crimson velvet curtains always brought back memories, however unlikely, of the wooden shed behind the Highlander pub where I had placed two jam jars as payment to get in, before my working days with Angus McDonald had made me rich.

I remembered the countless times I had run the projector for Mr McNab while he got hopelessly drunk and fell asleep, good memories, spoiled only by the shock of my indiscretion with Maggie that had landed me here.

Cherished memories always seemed to be brought to an abrupt end, by the picture of a tearful Maggie. I'd abandoned her in a cowardly act of self-preservation, and I wasn't proud of it. I dismissed it from my mind, and watched the heroes of the screen do everything right. Outside on the streets a kind of reckless gaiety was alive, and it was infectious. People scurried into the pubs during the black-out, where they kept each others' spirits up by singing defiantly while the doodle-bugs fell all around.

In the midst of a crisis we seemed able to poke fun at Adolph's manhood and laugh at Lord Haw-Haws attempt to spread despondency. Money was short, rations were shorter and nylons were impossible, but Ellen hated to go out without them.

'Draw me some seams George, I feel undressed without them.'

So she'd make me draw a black line down the back of her legs to resemble the seam of a stocking and then we'd get drunk on beer and sing so loudly that nothing could be heard. At the end of the night when the all-clear sounded we would stagger home, giving thanks for having escaped the carnage. With the same recklessness we'd throw caution to the wind and it was on just such a night that our second son Robert George was conceived.

We both hoped and prayed that the war might be over by the time our new baby showed his face and things would get back to normal. The daily broadcasts now were encouraging parents to send their children away to the relatively safe countryside. This mass evacuation had a dual purpose, the children would be safe and the parents would be free to work night and day if that was what was required. We watched them go in their droves, some as young as five clutching cardboard cases and with their names and destinations clearly stamped on the labels attached to their coats. Like parcels they went, in a daze, to places and a kind of life town kids had never been used to.

Tearful parents waved them off, knowing there was no choice in the separation, and not knowing if they would ever see them again. The sight brought back memories of my own separation and the abandonment that I had felt, when closing the door on my family life. It was something that had hurt me deeply and had never quite healed. I could imagine their fears and feel again the hot tears on my cheeks as I strode away from my childhood, frightened, lonely and deserted by all who had said that they loved me. Those feelings crept over me again now and my heart went with them. The stations were crammed with children, who were told they were going on holiday, and in a holiday mood they steamed away.

Our Stewart was too young to be separated from Ellen, so he stayed. I couldn't and wouldn't have let him go, not while I had breath in my body. No child of mine would ever know that feeling of loss, we would stand or fall together. Ellen was a brave girl, too brave for my shredded nerves. She took too many risks and the more I saw of the devastation, the more worried I became. Just two streets away a block of houses were levelled and this was the last straw for me. I put my foot down—she'd have to go, down the nearest shelter, or home to Norfolk and I'd have no more argument about it.

'Alright George, but I'm not happy. If it settles your nerves we'll go. Lucy will look after you, so you won't miss me.'

'Of course I will,' though truth to tell, I didn't know just how much. She went scurrying back to Norfolk as I breathed a sigh of relief. The silence she left behind her and the absence of the baby's chatter that I'd become so used to, left me with the loneliest feeling, but I was sure I'd been right to send them away and I could concentrate, as Dada had, on staying alive.

The next few weeks raced by. I worked harder and longer than ever, volunteering for extra duties, fire-fighting until I was fit to drop and leaving no time to dwell on my loneliness or on how this nightmare might finally end. We were losing men on my shift, tiredness breeds mistakes and our alertness to the dangers didn't register as well on our second or third night. Our reactions were slower and our desperation to dig people out of burning buildings forced us to take chances and unacceptable risks. Bert Capstick was my fire-fighting mate, older than me and a whole lot steadier. He lived in a nice block of flats with his wife and little girl, and we worked our shifts together. Bert and I looked after each other and we both agreed that four pairs of eyes were a lot better than two. He had saved me from walking into danger several times and he would admonish me for being reckless. He was the restraining hand that stopped me diving in after a cry for help without first assessing the pitfalls. Tonight it was raining fit to drown a rat, and the noise it made against our helmets blotted out the signals we looked for when searching an unstable building. I heard a child's cry.

'Steady boy,' Bert said, reaching for me. But impulsiveness was my middle name and I dived in. She was trapped beneath a table that had taken the force of the fallen roof. I shone my torch down between the wooden joists and I could see her and her unconscious mother lying beneath. God forgive me for panicking, but it could have been Ellen and Stewart, and against all good sense I tore at the debris.

I heard Bert's alarmed shout and from instinct, and with the help of a push from Bert, I rolled away from the falling masonry. Bert, bless him, took a hit. He had saved my life but the falling wall had caught his leg, and now I dug with raw hands to free him.

'Leave me George, see to the child. My leg's broke, but I'll live.'

I dug like a man possessed until I could drop down to where the mother lay. Thankfully they weren't trapped but the table was threatening to collapse under the weight. I lifted the little girl, who was clinging to her mother, out from under the haven that had protected them and up toward Bert who was just able to reach into the gap and hoist the child up.

He wouldn't be able to help with the woman so I had to try to revive her. She looked unhurt and was still breathing, but she may have taken a blow to the head in the initial fall. I used my water bottle to splash water on her face and gently called her. She moaned and tried to rise,

'My baby,' she screamed, seeing the empty space beside her.

'She's alright but we have to get you out. The whole building is unsafe.'

'Mummy,' she heard the child scream.

From somewhere she found the strength to crawl out and reach up through the gap to touch the hand of her child. I hoisted her up and she clawed her way to where Bert was hanging on to the hysterical child. I followed her up and together we freed Bert's leg and I tied a crude splint to hold it.

We sat in the pouring rain awaiting help, soaked to the skin but alive to see another day, for which we all thanked Almighty God. I managed to flag down a passing taxi, and explained our need was greater than the yanks he was picking up from a dance.

'Let the buggers get their pretty uniforms wet,' I said.

'I can just see them standing on the pavement, dripping wet, not knowing if I'm coming or not,' he laughed.

He whisked them off to hospital and I trudged back to fill out my report.

My boss told me to take some leave.

'George I don't want to see you here tomorrow or you'll be another corpse for us to shift, as if there isn't enough already.'

I went home reluctantly and sat in Lucy Simpkin's kitchen and Dada's words came back to me, 'Geordie,' he'd said, 'I've been forced to witness Man's Inhumanity to Man, and for what I was part of, I hope God can forgive us all.' It had scarred his mind and this would scar mine. I had dragged whole families from the wreckage of bombed houses and my heart went out to the soldiers returning from the front only to find their families wiped out. I forced myself as he had, to put these feelings to the back of my mind and think about my own little family and how lucky I was to have them safely tucked away in the country.

Lucy came in and found me with my head in my hands, and bless her, she took me in hand. She'd been parted from her John for months, with no news to cheer her, but she still had room in her heart for me. Within half an hour we'd agreed that I should catch the first available train in the morning to King's Lynn and see my family. It would be worth it just to see Ellen again and to prove to her mother that I wanted the best for her and Stewart. I hurried my way to the station early next morning, and travelled impatiently to King's Lynn and on again to Bircham, determined to be reunited with my own little family.

I caught Ellen pushing an old pram up the lane toward home, and I watched her, not wanting to break the spell that this vision cast on me. She looked so happy, smiling down at Stewart that I hesitated for a moment. She must have had a sixth sense because she suddenly looked back and her eyes lit up, as if a prayer had been answered.

'George, is that you?' she squealed.

'It had better be me, or some tinker's standing here, wearing my best suit.'

My humour had been just the right thing to lighten the moment, she giggled to chase away the tears. I opened my arms and she ran to me.

Mrs Griffin, despite my fears, was glad to see me and I slotted back in as if I'd never been away. Once again I'd read the script wrong, and although baffled, my spirits soared.

'Now, come and sit down. Dinner will be five minutes and you can give us the chapter and verse on your intentions toward my daughter and grandson.'

'George, I'm coming back with you,' Ellen blurted out. 'I should never have left. It was the reason we married as quickly as we did, so we could remain together.'

'I forbid you to do any such thing Ellen,' Mrs Griffin said, banging her hand on the table.

For once I agreed, 'What about the baby?' I asked.

'My baby goes with me, and I go with you. Book us on to the next train and we'll leave tonight—and don't give me that look George, or you mum, I've made up my mind.'

This wasn't what I wanted, wasn't what I'd come for, God forbid. She was pregnant and with a toddler to look after. I hadn't expected this and I didn't know what else I could say to dissuade her. I tried by recounting some of the most gruesome scenes we'd encountered, but after hours of argument I could see I wasn't going to change her mind. I just hoped that we wouldn't live to regret it.

We spent the night talking about the war, work, and where I lived. They finally talked us into staying the night and although deep down I wished I could magic myself back to work and leave Ellen safely stored here, it was not to be. I cursed my impulsiveness that had made me come here without thinking. The memories of Shanny sleeping in the same room kept me awake but I could look back now on the fun we'd had for the first time without tears. The house was empty when I woke, save for Mrs Griffin and Evelyn, and after a quick breakfast we walked to the station. In no time at all, we were back in the bomb zone.

We arrived at Lucy's and were greeted with a smile and a note requesting me to see the works manager first thing in the morning. It was welcome news—we'd been allocated a flat and though Ellen was sorry to leave her dear friend Lucy, we needed the space. Bert had put a word in for me when the flat above his had become vacant and strings had been pulled. Robert George was born amid the confusion of moving on St Georges Day, 23rd of April and we raced back to Lucy's. Thank the Lord for angels like Lucy Simpkin, she was a gift from heaven in the midst of a crisis. Robert seemed keen to enter this chaotic world of conflict and his appearance signalled yet another massive onslaught. Our moving was postponed while mother and child gained strength and glad I was to have Ellen looked after while I worked night and day. Ellen pestered me to get her home ready and every moment I could spare I spent gathering together furniture — what we could salvage from the wreckage of houses which had once been homes, and what I could afford from the local second-hand shop.

Ellen scolded me, 'It's like robbing a grave' she said, 'taking someone else's possessions while they're away.'

'It's needs must,' I told her.

I didn't like to tell her the truth that we'd pulled the dead occupants from the house, or she would have rather gone without.

The flat was new and spacious and the block was occupied mostly by women whose husbands were away on active service so I found myself being lent to anyone and everyone, to fix and mend, lift and move, whenever I had any free time. Bert's wife Marge was a great help to Ellen and tried to encourage her to use the purpose built concrete air-raid shelter that was within easy reach of our block of flats, but Ellen refused.

The rest of the occupants would file down when the air-raid siren blasted out the warning and despite mine and Marge's insistence, she wouldn't go.

'I'm not taking Stewart and Robert down into that concrete coffin, Stewart's got Asthma and the damp will be worse for him than anything the Germans can throw at us.' In all truth I think she was frightened of being buried alive, so they sat under our Formica topped kitchen table while the bombs fell all around. Ellen would sing to drown out the whistling sound of the bombs and the deadly silence that followed, pacifying Stewart while feeding Robert, while I was left to worry. Every day the bombing seemed worse, the buildings left standing around us were now fewer than those that had been reduced to rubble and with more dead and injured each day, I felt more like an undertaker than a carpenter. We were living alongside a graveyard, amongst the wreckage of a once-peaceful suburb. Our work at DeHavilland was going at full speed and despite being permanently tired I felt we were beginning to hold our own. Our fighters were protecting the Aerodrome from bombing raids and with the help of better machinery we were turning out planes faster than ever.

Thank God we were all unhurt and blessed with good luck. I

brooded in my breaks between fire-fighting and building planes on how long our luck could last.

'I'm sticking to you like shit to a blanket George. You've been blessed by the Gypsy's boy,' Bert would say.

If he knew the truth of that statement I'm not sure it would have mattered to him, in wartime petty things like background were the least of our problems. I was still worried sick that someone like me would drag my family from a pile of rubble and shrug with practised detachment? I began to regret that I had let Ellen have her way, but Bert kept me on track and out of trouble.

We were living in fast changing times and ration books dominated our lives and our meals. There was precious little fresh food and a diet of Spam was a shock to our systems after the rabbit and pheasant we'd been used to. The reality was that living in the wild like Dada, or in the country like Mrs G, though poor we had had the chance of fresh meat or fish, but in a city we had to settle for Spam. Ellen had to take the children and queue for hours when she heard through the grapevine that a delivery to the local butcher was due.

'George get the pram down the stairs, I've got to go,' she shouted. 'I'm meeting Lucy and Marge, and we have to be near the front or the mince will all be gone.' The thought of real meat made my mouth water.

'Watch out for falling rubble,' I said, knowing the dangers presented by the unstable buildings that were everywhere. 'Walk in the middle of the road if you can.'

'You fuss too much,' she shouted as she pushed her way up the road.

I'd seen too many fire-fighters injured when the vibration of a passing lorry caused a damaged house to fall. I'd rather eat Spam for the rest of my life than have her take any more chances. I couldn't stop her, she was too strong-willed and I couldn't afford to dwell on it when I was scrabbling among the wreckage, or I'd be the one buried.

I made my way home after another hideous night full of injured and dead adults, of crying, lost children wandering the street, orphaned by the indiscriminate destruction. I arrived to find a meal fit for a king adorning the table and candles lighting the room. Tears sprung to my eyes, knowing that Ellen had battled her way to spend her rations on me.

'It's our anniversary George, and I wasn't going to let it pass without a celebration.'

Amidst all the chaos I had remembered. How could I forget? I had bartered a pair of nylons from an American soldier, who was planning to bribe his way into some young girl's affections. This hadn't gone down too well with our boys and he'd got himself into a fight and was ready to let his prize go.

'George where on earth…?' She squealed.

'Best if you don't ask.' I said

We hugged, ate our meal and made love as the sirens blasted out a warning that we ignored. It was a special memory that I will never forget.

My only relief from the daily slaughter came at night. I could dream of the wild, lonely Highlands, and pictured Ellen and the boys there, safe from this crazy world. Better to be a tinker, wandering in the heather and living off the land, than have the respectability that had driven me on and into this daily nightmare. What stopped me from grabbing Ellen and running off to her family, or mine, I'll never know. Surely, I told myself, it could get no worse and an end would soon be in sight, and it did seem that the bombing was becoming more isolated, and the radio boasted that we were winning the battle for the skies.

This speculation lifted our spirits, but if it were the truth or just wishful thinking, was anybody's guess. We had less German bombers reaching us, but if you wanted to be morbid you'd listen to talk of a rocket-propelled bomb called the V2 that could destroy large areas and be launched from France just the other side of, what seemed like a very narrow strip of water. But what brought me out in the shivers was the thought of being struck down in sight of the finishing line. Some of my workmates took to the drink, having pulled one too many bodies from their burning homes. Families like mine, whose sheer bad luck had placed them directly beneath a plane that had lightened its load on the way home from a raid.

Our life was full of 'if onlys,' and giving thanks every night for seeing another day and hoping the news would break that this hideous destruction had come to an end. Like my father before me, I prayed every night for the end to come, and as if in answer to my prayer, one evening the news we'd longed for was shouted from our little radio. I was sitting down to my dinner, when the second war in my lifetime ended.

'George did you hear that?'

I nodded as we sat in shock, unable to speak. The silence was unnerving. It took a full minute to absorb what we'd been waiting impatiently for, for the past five years. We hugged each other, we hugged the children and we even hugged the furniture.

'Bless,' she said as she kissed the Formica-topped table that had been her family's shelter during the terrifying bombing raids. I truly think we were temporarily out of our minds, all the worries were lifted and we became hysterical. The door was being hammered by an excited fist and as I opened it, I was dragged out to join the celebrations. There were tears and laughter and beer saved for such an occasion. It was a time spent reflecting on those who hadn't survived and celebrating with those who had.

§

Robert McPhee

Chapter Ten

A Time to Reflect

Once again my passion got the better of me and in the joy of peacetime Ellen conceived our third child. Patricia Anne was born and she was the icing on the cake for me. She was beautiful like her mother, with my raven black hair and her mother's pale skin.

'You're prejudiced,' Ellen said. Prejudice had something to do with it. We were complete now and I felt blessed. The next couple of years were spent clearing the ground and building homes for the returning troops. I was still working for de DeHavilland and they reserved me a house in a new estate being built at Elstree, within walking distance of the factory.

It was our first proper house, brand new, and Ellen was over the moon. We had a large garden to grow our own vegetables and we were surrounded by fields, not unlike her own beloved Norfolk. It would have been perfect but for the location. I knew she missed her mother. She had become just as cut off from her family as I had from mine, and I began to understand how the war had severed the threads that had bound families together. I knew, without transport, we would remain estranged, and I realised that life would never be the same for her. Although I knew what isolation felt like, I had had her family as a substitute. For Ellen, it was just me and the children, and I hoped it would be enough.

We'd made a life for ourselves and we were surrounded by people in the same situation. I had become the George McPhee I'd set out to be, a respectable working man with a wonderful family. Yet, at times, I would take myself off to my shed in the garden and let loose the raggy-arsed tinker boy lurking inside, to take me racing back across the heather, where I secretly romped with Jonno, Charlie and Maggie Crook. I'm embarrassed to admit, I'd hear her soft brogue, which would set the hairs on my neck standing on end and feel again the shock waves of my departure. I'd be off on a trail of questions that I would never know the answers to.

I promised myself that I'd go back some day and meet again the people I'd left behind, to show them all that I'd made a success of my life. But if I did go, I'd go alone. I had dreams of riding back in a posh car, drawing up at my mother's door and seeing my Dada puffed up with pride. All the people I knew would whisper that the runaway tinker boy had found his pot of gold and had fulfilled his mother's dreams. The wish to return seemed always to be buried in my subconscious, but when I let my guard down, the tinker boy, Geordie, would pop out to remind me who I was and where I'd come from and the wish to return triumphant was transformed into a desire I found hard to resist.

Ellen would catch me daydreaming and quickly guessed there was a lot of myself that I wouldn't, or couldn't, share with her. She had grown to be very proper, like her mother, and although she had made little of my past, she was becoming mindful of what her new friends and neighbours might think. So she didn't ask, and I didn't say any more about my family—they remained tucked firmly in the recesses of my mind. Our time now was filled with our growing children, and as they grew, I could see my heritage peeking through.

The black hair and olive skin they shared with my family, and little flashes of Geordie appeared in the boys' behaviour. I was tempted to talk about my youth, perhaps I should have done, but something restrained me.

I wanted to spare them the prejudice that came with being a traveller. I admonished myself for feeling ashamed of my birthright and my family, but I still couldn't face the truth, so the children were warned not to answer the door to tinkers.

'George shoo them off,' Ellen would say. 'And don't go buying any rubbish.'

So I'd wave them away and slip them five bob. It was a mistake because they knew then that I was a soft touch and they wouldn't knock unless they saw my old car standing outside. I don't to this day know if my reputation was passed on from tinker to tinker but I could see they were glad it was me who had answered the door. I was sure, it became common knowledge and as the tinkers were gradually replaced by Sikhs, I was their number one target.

They were strange people with their large turbans and broken English, carrying huge suitcases filled to the gunnels with everything from bootlaces to hair-restorer. They would knock and step to the side of the porch. They were crafty and somehow sensed that Ellen would peek through the curtains before she'd open the door. She'd call me to answer it if she wasn't sure and remind me that if it was anyone selling anything that we were not interested. The Sikhs took selling to a different level and they were impossible to say no to, once they had their cases open. I invariably bought a bar of soap or something useless just to get rid of them. I couldn't snub them, in another place, another time it might be my own Dada. They brought back memories of the hours we spent following Dada around the streets of Wick carrying pots of all descriptions he'd made to sell, and snubbing them would be like snubbing him and that would hurt, so I remained, I admit it, 'a soft touch.'

God save us, though, from inquisitive children. They began to ask questions about their grand-parents in Scotland which I was reluctant to answer. I fended them off with snippets to satisfy their curiosity. But there was no satisfying Tricia. I couldn't stir her interest by telling only part of my life's story, it was all or nothing. So I chose to invent little stories to satisfy her and I hoped my father would understand and I wouldn't come to regret it. I had escaped from the taunts and insults of my own childhood, and I was determined to spare her the unhappiness that could bring, so we shared a few harmless stories about old Jen.

It was lovely to talk about my dear friend, who'd dragged me from the Latheron Workhouse through driving snow on my first day in this life. I told of her gentle eyes and velvet muzzle, of her beautiful tail for hanging onto when I was tired, and the milking of Jezebel as she mewed softly. I admit to a tear rising in my eye and a lump forming in my throat at the vision I painted for her, but I was careful to keep little tinker boy Geordie hidden lest she would feel disappointed in me.

We were settled now and my new job at the Associated British Film Studios gave me an outlet for my restlessness. My make-and-mend techniques were well suited to the demands of the mock-up film sets I was required to build. Best of all, I was able to travel to locations all over the world. It cured a desire buried deep in me, to move on and over the next hill.

'So while you're away rubbing shoulders with the rich and famous for months at a time, I'm left to struggle with three spirited children,' is what Ellen said.

This, of course, didn't go down very well, but the money was good, and each time I came home I'd bring presents for all, and money for Ellen to spend on the house. For me I felt the pride of success, exotic places, the best hotels and lots of money.

One location had taken me to Africa on a film called The Naked and the Dead set in the Kenya National Park. The work was hard and the hours long and it didn't come without risks.

Working in the jungle and being exposed to malaria-carrying mosquitoes was the least of our problems. We'd launched a raft that housed a camera crew, whose job it was to follow a twin raft down the river, taking shots of a hippopotamus needed for a scene, when the unthinkable happened. The huge beast turned, butted the lead raft, causing a man to fall into the river. He was never seen again. It gave us the shivers. I left this incident out of my letters home, to avoid a panic. What they didn't know wouldn't harm them.

In the evenings I'd sit in the sun and dream. I'd close my eyes and try to measure how far I'd come from my roots.

I could hardly believe that the George McPhee lying here in the African sun, was the same person as little Geordie who had shivered himself to sleep in Angus's barn.

In Wick life would be following a familiar pattern. Jonno would be the same rascal he had always been, I guessed, doing the same things Jonno always did and Charlie would have followed him down that same road. I was, I reminded myself, drawn from the same womb as Jonno and Charlie and deep down I was still the little tinker boy who had fitted between them in our solitary bed. An act of fate had cast me to the wind and but for Angus's 'make and mend skills,' Maggie Crook and my enforced flight, I would not be rubbing shoulders with the stars of the silver screen. I had found my window of opportunity and had been forced to leap through it, and as I lay there I resolved finally to go and show Dada what they had all helped to make possible.

At home the gleaming blue and black MG Magnate standing outside my house was proclaiming to the street that I had 'arrived,' and was a man of substance. It was the last in a long line of vehicles I'd saved hard for. My tin had been full again, just like the old days, but this time nothing could prize it away from me, and I was determined to have my status symbol. It was the one extravagance that Ellen had agreed to, and although she managed me and my money very well and kept me from being foolish, she said a man of substance like me should have a car of quality. I think that's what I loved about her she'd never deny me my dream. Ellen was very proud of our status symbol, and I'd catch her peeking out of the window to watch the neighbours' admiring glances as they walked by and she would smile with satisfaction if they looked her way.

She was as pleased as I was to ride out in it, looking like royalty and with the smell of leather and the walnut veneer.

I'd started with an old motorbike during the war and with petrol on ration I'd managed to get some aviation fuel from work. Ellen said I looked like a cannonball being fired down the road with flames belching out the back, and was fearful I'd take off. It soon burned my engine out though and I settled for a succession of old cars that I was forever underneath, that is until now. My desire to go home in my posh car remained strong, but my resolve, not to put it off weakened. Our life was too busy right now so it still remained just a dream.

Ellen and I had settled and were living a quite different life than either of us had imagined we would. The children were growing and our life ebbed and flowed with no more thought given to our families or our past life. We only had time for the future. I was proud of what we'd achieved. We never shared our thoughts on how we came to this point, I had my memories and Ellen had hers. We had our weekly Sunday visits from Lilly and Ted, and occasionally from Len and Laurie, so Ellen was satisfied.

§

Robert McPhee

Chapter Eleven

Geordie's Return

News that my mother had died left me feeling guilty. She had wanted better for me and I had repaid her by deserting them and salving my conscience by sending a little money as often as I could. I decided I must go now before my Dada slipped away and show him that their gift of freedom had been a great success. Ellen and I rowed about my going alone, but I went anyway. I travelled by train, I didn't have it in me to show off especially if Jonno and Charlie were there and things were the same as I'd left them. I went shame-faced bearing gifts, a long lost son trying to make up for the missing years, with a feeling it was 'too little too late.'

My first glimpse of Dada made me feel that I'd never been away. He was smaller in stature than I remembered, but the aura surrounding him still filled the room. We hugged away the years and he whispered to me that I looked older than himself and he asked how I had let time steal away my hair. His house had replaced the cabin I remembered, and gone was the cart and old Jen, but the man remained and I could hardly speak. I took off my sheepskin coat and draped it around his shoulders, and we sat and talked of all the things I'd missed and family events where my place had been laid just in case I'd come.

'Never a day passed when yer mother didn't speak of her little runaway and praised God for fulfilling her dream of a new life for ye. We heard from time to time of your exploits, things you omitted from your letters. Stories from wandering tinkers who'd worked on the road gang. We had a visit from the big Irishman, Liam, and we knew from him ye'd moved on and that ye'd grown in ti a fine man…Ah,' he said, suddenly remembering, 'Liam brought yer diary with him and I saved it for ye. We never could bring ourselves ti have it read, and so it's laid here, waiting for ye ti come.'

'Let it lay, Dada.' All my growing up years were held securely in its pages, my struggle to overcome my own beginnings. I'd finally come to realise, you are what you are, and though you may try to change, your genes will never let you go.

'Dada, I've come ti say thank you. Everything I am, I owe ti you and mam, and I'm so sorry I didn't come before. Was she hurt that I was so ungrateful? I wanted to come. I'd come running back across the heather in my dreams, to see you both, whenever I had troubles. I'd hear your wise words and feel my mother's love and wake the next day with new strength.'

'Aye,' he sighed. He patted my head as he'd done whenever I'd been in trouble.

'Dada, I have a family. Ellen's my wife's name, and three children.'

'Yes, I know.'

'I've two boys, Stewart and Robbie, and a daughter, Patricia.'

I pulled out a photograph and he smiled at the family likeness.

'What did ye say, Dada?' I'd stumbled on as if he'd said nothing. 'Did ye say ye knew?'

'Aye,' he nodded, 'at least about yer wife, Ellen. Her sister, Nora, and husband Eric, came ti see us while they were posted at the base, during the war, and we had a long chat.'

'She knows then that we're tinkers?'

'Aye and cared less. She's a fine young girl if a bit hare 'em scare 'em.'

My heart missed a beat, 'You didn't say why I left, Dada?'

'Your secret's safe with me, Geordie,' was all he said on the matter.

'Ye canny run away from yer genes, Geordie, that's plain ti see,' he said, looking again at the photograph of the children. I nodded. I had come to the same conclusion but by a very different route.

'Next time I come, Dada, I promise I'll bring them, but this time I have something I have to settle and I must do that alone.'

'Settle it then, boy, and come back ti me, I've lots to tell.'

I left him and strolled down to the harbour. The place was unchanged. The seat was still there where we'd sat, me and Charlie suffering our drunkenness, awaiting our penny treat. I looked over at the alley and the same feelings of excitement that made me tremble then were making my hands shake now. Try as I may to make a smoke, my trembling fingers made as ragged a roll-up as I'd made the day Maggie had come to me. I pushed it into my mouth to stop myself from calling out.

I walked to McReedie's and bought a bag of her favourite sweets and a small bunch of flowers, and made my way to her father's house.

He would be gone now, of course, but there was a good chance she would still be there. Unlike me, the people of Wick don't move far from their home voluntarily.

As I approached the house, I felt my destiny calling me. I had finally to know if I had another child in this world. What I'd do if I had, at this moment, was of no consequence. I rapped on the door and waited. I wondered, would I know the brown-eyed beauty of my youth or not? The door finally opened and she stood there, 'Maggie Crook a penny-a-look' with her hair showing flecks of grey but with the same beautiful eyes that had been the cause of my flight, the catalyst that changed my person from Geordie to George.

§

Chapter Twelve

Maggie's Confession

'Hello, Geordie, I heard ye were back, how are ye, boy? Have ye tuppence in yer pocket, or is this a social call?'

I smiled stiffly at her banter, and followed her into her small front room and sat down uncomfortably. I stared around the room as she busied herself, making tea, and caught sight of a picture on the mantelpiece. For the life of me it could have been my Tricia. My heart sank as I stared, mesmerised at the likeness. She came with the tea and could see me staring fixedly at the picture.

'Maggie, I need you to tell me if the child was mine. I've waited thirty years to know and now finally I've come.'

'Aye' she sighed, 'carrying a bag of my favourite sweets, a bunch of flowers, and weighed down with a prickly conscience, boy. That's Tess,' she said, picking up the photograph I'd been staring at. 'Taken it was on her first day at school. She's a clever girl, my Tess. She teaches at our old school now. Not like me, expelled at fifteen, she loved school, like her dad.'

I must have looked suitably stunned. She was having her pound of flesh.

'She was mine then,' I stuttered.

'You weren't the only clever boy in Wick with tuppence in his pocket, Geordie. It was a wicked girl's trick I played on ye boy, it was all to have yer tin. Jonno had boasted of yer fortune, so I padded me waist, took the abuse, and got meself away from school with your fortune. Two weeks later, I fell pregnant for real, with me fisherman, and the story I'd started became true. He married me and was a fine husband. He drowned, poor man, in a storm off the point five years since.'

I was angry and relieved all at the same time, my flight, the loss of my family, the birth of my new identity, all for my twenty pounds in pennies. I gave her the sweets and got up to leave.

'She's all I've got left, Geordie,' she said, looking again at the photograph.

I followed her gaze and saw something I couldn't put my finger on, and left. I never met Tess. It would have been a mistake to test the truthfulness of her story, so I let go at last of the guilt and was ready to go home.

§

Chapter Thirteen

George Buries His Past

I reflected, while waiting at the station, on my conversations with Dada.

Jonno had a houseful of children, thirteen at the last count, in Pittlochry, and all kept spotlessly clean by his wife. Charlie lived close by and they were well known and well liked, but scrappers when they'd had a drink. Hughie was unmarried and Jeannie was living with and looking after Dada. Sarah was the sister I had never seen, she was married and living in Wick.

The train arrived and I chose an empty carriage. Together, we gazed through the window, the 'raggy-arsed tinker boy' and me. We watched the pink-clad hills flash by, hills that had once been our home. And as we sped south, we talked of the cold snow on our feet going to school in the winter and the tattie pie we shared in the dark days of the Depression. Dada's tinker stew and old Jen with a muzzle as soft as velvet, Mam's biscuits, and Aunt Elisabeth's whiskey massage and of Tam MacKay's wise words as sharp now as they had been then. I needed no more reminding of who I was, or where I'd come from. My conscience was clear and maybe at last I could share these things with the people I loved. But as the thought passed and the train crossed the border, I knew I never would.

§

Author's Note

The sudden death of my father, George, was the most traumatic experience I'd ever had to face. He'd seemed so indestructible. The shock of his leaving without ever filling in the blank spots in his life hit me even as the news sunk in. His heart had exploded in the blink of an eye as my mum had served his dinner, and I cried for the loss of the man and the memories. Those memories began and ended for us with our family, which was brought starkly into focus by the arrival of his sister, Jean. The dispute she brought with her, as to what his wishes were and how and where he should be laid to rest, came as an unwelcome surprise. She demanded his burial in Scotland in the clan cemetery.

'It's what Geordie would have wanted,' she said to us.

My mother would have none of it and was determined to lay him to rest in the local churchyard. This insignificant wrangle set my mind on a trail of thought. I didn't recognise the man my aunt was talking about. Who was this highland-born Geordie McPhee who had never showed himself fully to us, his children? In the midst of our grief, I knew that I would have to find him and get to know him and his life before I could move on.

I was full of good intentions, but they were pushed to one side during the weeks of mourning. It was perhaps a year or more before I could talk about him to my mum. I finally decided to ask a few general questions about his early life, but I was disappointed with the results. Mum had a way of stonewalling when she faced an issue that was either too private or caused her to rake over old wounds. I didn't feel I could push her, so my efforts came to a premature end, and with the demands of everyday life, the quest was pushed out of my mind and I never again broached the subject with her.

It may seem that I was easily put off, but I think she had a memory of her George that she wanted undisturbed, and I respected that.

Ellen, beloved wife of George and dear mother to me, had a further eight wonderful years, and although lonely without him to look after, she enjoyed her time with the family and we occasionally saw the lively girl who had captivated him in their youth. All my teenage life I had seen her as a peacemaker who would do anything for a quiet life, a smoother of tempers and a selfless mother. Now she showed me the woman hidden inside the mother and it did my heart good to see her as my dad had.

My mum passed away in her sleep and my despair was complete.

It was while my sister, Patricia, and I were sorting through their effects that we came across my father's birth certificate—a document we had never seen in our life before and one that would shock us all. That small piece of paper kick-started my search and lead me to my roots. I read it and reread it. Here at last was the secret so jealously kept from us: our tinker heritage in faded black and white. This hardly legible document was signed with a cross by Robbie, my grandfather, and his first cousin, Sarah—my grandmother. Geordie, our father, was born in mid-winter it said, in a workhouse at Latheron several miles from Wick, and that small snippet, gave us the first piece of the puzzle. The rest of the pieces that completed the picture lead us a merry dance from his hometown of Wick, to his later home in

England and to what remained of his family.

I was determined to ferret them out and I persuaded my older brother, Stewart, home from South Africa, to join me in a quest to find our family, for better or for worse. Together we set out by train, and as we clicked our way North of the border, I tried hard to feel as though I was going home. I let my mind race freely across the purple heather and imagined this tinker man Robbie with his cart, in the bitter February temperatures, making a headlong dash for the Latheron Workhouse in time for my father's birth. My journey was a voyage of discovery that explained many of my deepest feelings— inherited traits that were not attributable to my suburban life. This discovery caused us all to adjust our lives and take a fresh look at ourselves and the man who broke the travelling mould to become George McPhee, our father.

The book you have just read is the result of that journey, and although it is a work of fiction, it is based on as many facts as I could find and all parts of the main plot are certainly true. My father George had laid his ghost to rest, and I had walked in his footsteps to uncover the secret he so jealously guarded. It's true to say his secret robbed Stewart, Patricia and me of our grandparents and the reality of who we truly are. But seen through his eyes, I think I understand his reasons. I know now I had grandparents to be proud of, whose greatest sacrifice was to give up their second son, to tread his own path through life, follow a dream, and to escape the limits of a travellers' life.

He realised that dream at his grandson's graduation, and I like to imagine him smiling, along with the raggy-arsed tinker boy peeping over his shoulder for the very last time.

Rest in Peace George

Geordie McPhee.